HERBS

DETAILED PLANT GUIDE • 500 PHOTOGRAPHS • RECIPES AND CRAFTS

HERBS

DETAILED PLANT GUIDE • 500 PHOTOGRAPHS • RECIPES AND CRAFTS

WELDON
OWEN

Published by Weldon Owen
Kings Road Publishing, a division of Bonnier Publishing
3.08 The Plaza, 535 Kings Road,
London, SW10 0SZ
Copyright © 2011 Weldon Owen

Managing Director Kay Scarlett
Publisher Corinne Roberts
Creative Director Sue Burk
Images Manager Trucie Henderson
Senior Vice President, International Sales Stuart Laurence
Sales Manager, North America Ellen Towell
Administration Manager, International Sales Kristine Ravn
Production Director Todd Rechner
Production and Prepress Controller Mike Crowton
Production Controller Lisa Conway
Production Coordinator Nathan Grice

Designer Adam Walker
Editor Elizabeth Ginis
Editorial Assistant Natalie Ryan
Indexer Tricia Waters

Printed by 1010 Printing
Manufactured in China

The paper used in the manufacture of this book is sourced
from wood grown in sustainable forests. It complies with the
Environmental Management System Standard ISO 14001:2004

A WELDON OWEN PRODUCTION

DISCLAIMER

This book is intended as a reference
volume only, not as a medical manual or
guide to self-treatment. The information
that it contains is general, not specific
to individuals and their particular
circumstances, and is not intended to
substitute for any treatment that may
have been prescribed by your physician.
Any plant substance, whether ingested
or used medicinally or cosmetically,
internally or externally, can cause an
allergic reaction in some people. The
publishers cannot be held responsible
for any injury, damage or otherwise
resulting from the use of herbal
preparations. We strongly caution you
not to try self-diagnosis or attempt
self-treatment for serious or long-term
problems without consulting a qualified
medical practitioner. Always seek
medical advice promptly if symptoms
persist. Never commence any self-
treatment while you are undergoing a
prescribed course of medical treatment
without first seeking professional advice.

CONTENTS

GROWING HERBS

WHAT ARE HERBS?

The terms "herb" and "herbaceous" are often confused but generally a herb is a plant valued for its flavor, scent, or medicinal properties.

"Herbaceous" often refers to perennial plants that have a long-lived root system, non-woody foliage, and flowers that regenerate each growing season.

Botanically, a herb is a plant, usually succulent and soft, that does not develop woody tissue. There are many plants, however, that we think of and use as herbs that do not strictly fall into this category. Rosemary, for example, has woody stems but soft sprigs.

Many herbs, such as parsley, sage, rosemary, and thyme have both culinary and medicinal uses.

Aromatic bay leaves, cinnamon sticks, cardamom capsules, star anise, and juniper berries are all the product of herbs.

WHY GROW HERBS?

People have been growing herbs for thousands of years. Once an essential part of life, they were used to flavor and preserve food, and for medicinal and religious purposes.

Imagine how bland food would be without condiments and how dull cooking would become if we didn't experiment with herbs—a sprinkle of this and a dash of that.

Those keen cooks who are also good gardeners know the pleasure of growing these plants for their many wonderful qualities—beneficial, oil-filled, aromatic leaves, and tasty stems, fruits, and seeds.

VERSATILE HERBS
You can grow herbs for a variety of reasons. Use leaves in herbal medicines, fruits in the kitchen, flowers for beauty treatments, and taproots to dye cloth.

Herbs, such as aromatic dill, add flavor, spice, and zest to summer salads and winter hotpots.

Stock your home with fresh and dried herbs for culinary, medicinal, or craft purposes.

HERBS IN THE WILD

Herbs are a diverse group of plants that grow in all countries. They are used by indigenous peoples throughout the world.

As their culinary and medicinal qualities were appreciated, herbs became valuable commodities. Many species were taken to Britain by the conquering Romans as part of their provisions. Similarly, the Pilgrim Fathers took traditional herbs with them across the Atlantic before they discovered there were native herbs. Among them were sage and wormwood, which were burnt to purify air and repel insects. Native Northern Americans also used teasel, a plant now favored by cottage gardeners, as an eyewash and for the removal of warts.

BUSH FOODS

In Australia, indigenous vegetation has only recently been recognized by Europeans, who use the phrase "bush food" to distinguish edible plants.

Strongly scented wild thyme flowers are native to Europe and North Africa, and are used as an aphrodisiac.

Common herbs, including golden calendula, are often found growing amid a riot of colorful wildflowers.

BEWARE! POISON

Herbs give us delicious flavors, powerful fragrances, and remedies for various ills, but most can have dangerous side effects if taken in excess.

Herbs contain volatile oils that can be poisonous. In small doses they may contribute to our health, but are not a cure-all for serious diseases for which medical diagnosis and treatment must be sought. Some herbs are extremely poisonous and must never be ingested. These include foxglove and lily-of-the-valley. Be extremely careful when growing these plants around young children or animals.

All parts of foxglove are toxic and should never be eaten. It can cause nausea, vomiting, and blindness.

Lily-of-the-valley is a beautiful but poisonous herb, and must only be used by qualified practitioners.

CHOOSING A SITE

ACCESS
How you'll access your herbs is an important consideration. A wheelbarrow won't need much space between beds but a truck delivering soil certainly will.

Begin with a tour of your garden. If possible, always select a level site with good drainage because it is far easier to garden on flat surfaces.

Avoid hills that lose moisture quickly or areas where the soil is compacted and hard to dig. Stay away from pockets of low-lying land, where poor drainage and air circulation could encourage related diseases and pests. If you must garden on a slope, plant across it rather than up and down to prevent erosion.

Where garden space is limited, find a sunny spot and interplant a variety of herbs in the one container.

18

When choosing a site, consider the size and style of your garden, and the time you'll have to tend it.

DESIGNING YOUR HERB GARDEN

Regardless of the size, shape, or location of your garden, its style is a reflection of your taste and is limited only by your imagination and creativity.

The simplest gardens to set out and manage are square or rectangular ones. This is practical, as many blocks of land are boxlike. You may, however, choose to lay your garden beds following the curve of a hill, stream, fence, or wall, or design them to accent the shape of a building. Whatever design you choose, try it out on paper first and keep it simple.

ACHIEVING HARMONY
Include plants of mixed heights and sizes. Create a sense of rhythm too; repeat groupings of the same plant or use others with similar colors. For movement, let plants drift from front to back.

For easy access, plant in rows.

Symmetry suits formal gardens.

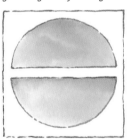

Use curves for cottage gardens.

Separate herbs into zones: culinary, medicinal, other.

Use common items, such as hoses, bins, buckets, gumboots, and shovels to map your garden layout.

Use common threads, a wending timber path or charming wicker boundary, to define garden zones.

A FORMAL HERB GARDEN

Formal landscapes use straight lines, sharp angles, and symmetrical plantings with a limited number of plants, usually low hedges of clipped evergreens.

The key to success with a formal garden is uniformity—you want the garden to be evenly spaced and developed. Plants are often repeated to form a mirror image. One of the most popular and traditional styles of herb-garden planting is the elaborate and formal knot garden, where herbs are interwoven with hedges for great effect.

Include a focal point, such as a sundial or bird bath, and boundaries. When building a wall, use materials that match your house. For hedges, choose species that will survive winter.

Straight paths suggest order and formality, and define garden spaces.

For a formal look include low, clipped hedges of lavender and rosemary, and symmetrical plantings and paths.

AN INFORMAL HERB GARDEN

Informal landscapes use curved lines to create a natural feel. They tend to have few permanent features, such as walls, and use a wide range of plants.

Informal designs are relaxed and lively, and are better suited to the small gardens of many of today's houses. Herbs can be planted in any part of the garden—beds, borders, containers.

The ultimate in informality, cottage gardens defy many gardening "rules": plants are packed closely together, colors aren't organized into different groupings, tall plants pop up in front of shorter ones, and flowers are allowed to grow through each other to create a delightful, casual mixture.

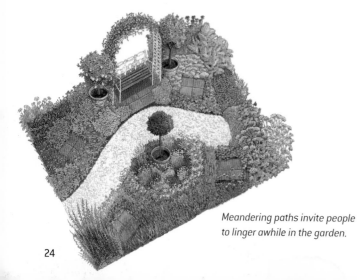

Meandering paths invite people to linger awhile in the garden.

Cottage gardens often include a relaxed mix of herbs, shrubs, containers, and borders.

A COOK'S HERB GARDEN

Herbs are a welcome addition to any kitchen. A garden brimming with flavorsome and aromatic herbs allows you to add personality to your dishes.

When designing your garden, consider herbs that transfer from garden to kitchen with aromatic ease. These include: Angelica, basil, bay, borage, caraway, chervil, chives, cilantro (coriander), dill, garlic, ginger, lemongrass, lovage, marjoram, mint, oregano, parsley, rosemary, sage, tarragon, and thyme.

Include different themes for different herbs; plant your culinary herbs together, near the kitchen for easy access, and separate to your medicinal or fragrant ones to avoid any confusion.

Pots interplanted with culinary herbs are a great addition to the kitchen; simply snip off foliage as required.

Popular cooking herbs, such as dill, chives, cilantro (coriander), basil, and sage, are also easy to grow.

CHOOSING YOUR PLANTS

You can choose herbs for your garden for their useful fruits and leaves, fragrant flowers, or perhaps for deep taproots that cope better with poor water supply.

If you want your herb garden to look good year round with minimal work, you may want to concentrate on perennials rather than annuals and biennials. Planting annuals, however, will give you more flexibility.

QUICK FIX
Annuals grow rapidly from seed, as do a few short-lived perennial herbs, including fennel, plantain, and vervain. Include these in your garden for quick color and flavor.

Visit your local garden center for healthy seedlings and advice on herbs that suit your needs.

ANNUALS

Annuals germinate, flower, set seed, and die all within one year. Easy to grow, they require full sun and plenty of water.

BIENNIALS

These herbs have a two-year lifespan. In the first year, they produce ample foliage and strong roots. In the second year, they flower, produce seeds, then die.

PERENNIALS

Perennials live for more than two years and make up the bulk of edible herbs.

Ideal for both hedges and pots, perennial lavender reaches its prime within 3–5 years of growth.

PROPAGATING HERBS

Propagation is a great way to increase your herb crops. Depending on the method, you can end up with dozens of new plants from a single specimen.

To propagate garlic, divide the largest cloves, plant 1 inch (2.5 cm) deep, and cover with compost.

DIVIDING

Dig around the perimeter of the plant's root system with a spade, then lift it all up. Set on the ground and divide by hand or with a trowel then replant in holes filled with fresh compost. Plants that send out underground rhizomes that sprout new plantlets can be divided without digging up the whole plant.

CUTTINGS

Take 3–5 inch (7.5–12.5 cm) cuttings of stem, just below the leaf joint and remove the lower leaves. Dip the base into rooting hormone, plant in a small pot with good drainage, and keep out of direct sun. After 6–8 weeks, check for visible roots. Place in the shade for a few days before planting out.

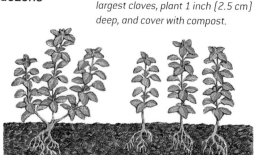

Dividing an existing plant is an easy and cost-effective way to start new ones. It can also rejuvenate old plants and make them more productive.

Some perennial herbs, such as sage, become straggly after a few years. Take cuttings in spring or summer to establish new plants.

SEED BANKING
To save seeds for future sowing, wait until they've matured on the plant. Hold the seedheads over a container and tap. Dry well and store in paper bags.

Clump-forming herbs, such as chives, are easily propagated by division in spring or fall.

CARING FOR YOUR PLANTS

Like other plants, herbs suffer from diseases, pests, and poor conditions. Knowing what they look like when they're healthy means you'll be able to spot any trouble.

> **DROUGHT-TOLERANT HERBS**
> In drier climates, grow burdock, catnip, chicory, lavender, hyssop, marjoram, oregano, pennyroyal, rosemary, rue, safflower, sage, and thyme.

WATERING

Gardens need about 1 inch (25 mm) of rainfall each week in average conditions. In most soils, one good soaking is better than several shallow waterings; it encourages roots to spread over a larger area and go deeper in search of water. Be careful not to overwater; excess fills the pore spaces in soil that would normally contain air.

If you have plenty of time, hand watering is ideal for small gardens, potted plants, and energetic gardeners.

Nourish herbs with compost, which releases organic nutrients, and they'll likely outcompete weeds.

WEEDING

Remove weeds before they grow large enough to compete with your plants for space, water, and nutrients. Start while preparing the garden bed; digging and hoeing will control many of the existing weeds until your plants fill out to cover the soil.

Mulching helps regulate soil temperature, prevents moisture evaporation, and adds nutrients.

INDOOR HERBS

MOISTURE MATTERS
Evaporation may be less indoors or more if your house is heated. Don't overwater; it encourages fungal disease and deprives roots of oxygen.

Surround yourself with fresh herbs year round. Cuttings taken in early fall will be ready to move into the garden in spring if you nurture them indoors all winter.

Your indoor herbs will need plenty of light each day for vigorous growth. A sunny windowsill is ideal; keep pots away from cold windows or drafts. Alternatively, buy a set of fluorescent light fixtures—a mix of cool white bulbs and red or blue lights—that are designed to imitate sunlight.

To maximize growth, leave a 6–8 inch (15–20 cm) gap between lights and seedlings.

Herbs flourish on sunlit windowsills and add color and scent to a room.

BALCONIES AND COURTYARDS

If you don't have room for garden beds, create a colorful oasis with container-grown plants on a balcony or in a courtyard or window box.

Herbs will thrive in containers if placed in a sunny position away from high winds.

Many of the most popular culinary herbs thrive in pots. Plant sun lovers such as basil, cilantro (coriander), dill, sage, rosemary, and thyme in the same tub.

Plant lemon balm, tansy, oregano, and parsley in partial shade; they tolerate as little as four hours of sun per day. Mint is ideal for containers; it is invasive in garden beds.

Large pots provide the best conditions for growth; they hold more soil, compost, nutrients, and water.

Always use a compost designed especially for container plants, and fertilize regularly in spring.

PREVENTING PESTS

BENEFICIAL BUGS
If you're lucky, beneficial insects, which have an appetite for harmful ones, will live among your garden's foliage and protect your plants.

Patrol your herb garden and look for early signs of insect damage. Learning to identify particular pests will help establish the best method of control.

The least disruptive pest-control methods, such as handpicking, spraying with water, or pruning, are most effective when used at the first sign of damage.

A highly effective way to correct up to 90 percent of disease and pest problems is to change the way you grow your plants. For example, if you've put a plant that prefers full sun in the shade, it may be weakened and unable to resist pests.

Caterpillars mainly satiate their voracious appetite with leaves, including those of Italian parsley.

38

Identify your bug. Colorado potato beetles, pictured, are garden pests, but ladybirds help control invaders.

PREVENTING PLANT DISEASES

Plant diseases are frustrating. Symptoms such as leaf wilt or stunted growth are often the only clues you'll have when trying to diagnose the problem.

PLANT PATHOGENS
Fungi are the most common cause of plant disease while *bacteria* infect plants through wounds and openings. *Viruses* are carried to plants by pests.

Your best defense is prevention. When buying new plants, inspect them carefully for signs of disease. Good sanitation practices are also essential. If you've been handling soil or plants that may be sources of infection, clean your boots and hands with a 5 percent solution of household bleach in water. Stay away from the garden during wet weather as many disease organisms require moisture for reproduction or mobility.

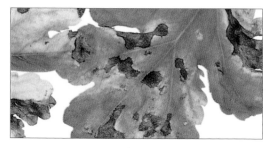

Downy mildew attacks leaves and causes yellow spots. Pick off and burn the affected leaves, then mulch and improve air flow through the plant.

Mosaic virus produces yellow to white streaks or mottling. Remove and burn the affected areas. If burning is prohibited, place in the rubbish bin.

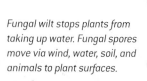

Fungal wilt stops plants from taking up water. Fungal spores move via wind, water, soil, and animals to plant surfaces.

Keeping your garden neat and free of debris helps to remove sites where pests and diseases can survive.

COMPANION PLANTING

Companion planting is the technique of combining plants that benefit each other. Use fragrant herbs in your garden to hide, repel, or trap pests.

Marigolds are popular companion plants. They attract beneficial insects and repel eelworms, which feed on peas, beans, carrots, cucumbers, and lettuce.

REPELLING WITH SMELLS

Many insects use their sense of smell to find their way to favored crops. Protect your plants by masking their scent with other powerful odors. Garlic, for example, releases deterrent aromas that ward off potato-eating insects and bugs, while onions prevent pests from attacking strawberries.

LURING PESTS

Some herbs have an almost irresistible appeal for certain pests and protect your crops in two ways. They act as a decoy, luring bugs away from desirable herbs, and concentrate them on a few plants, making them far easier to remove. Nasturtiums are excellent sacrifical plants because they are a favorite of aphids.

Many herbs, such as marigolds, lure pests away from vegetable and soft fruit crops and don't compete for nutrients or water.

GROWING COMMON HERBS

Common herbs are usually edible ones that people buy in the supermarket. Choose herbs you want to use and your garden is likely to thrive.

BUYING TIPS
Select small, healthy plants. Buy perennials before they bloom, so they can settle into the garden and establish roots. Avoid root-bound plants.

With both culinary and medicinal uses, and fragrant blossoms, hardy lavender is a favorite of gardeners.

The most common garden herbs include favorites such as basil, bay leaf, chives, garlic, dill, parsley, sage, and thyme.

Basil is great in tomato dishes and grows well in pots positioned on sunny windowsills. Bay leaf is great in soups and stews, while chives add flavor to potatoes, dips, and creamy soups. They grow up like a tall grass and are easily clipped when needed.

Garlic works in just about any savory dish and is a great garden addition, as are parsley, sage, and mint, the latter used as a tea.

Group herbs that have similar needs together, and don't forget to water and fertilize regularly.

HARVESTING HERBS

The first rule of harvesting herbs is to pick them early in the morning, just after the dew has dried but before the sun has had a chance to warm up.

Essential oils, which give herbs their flavor and fragrance, deteriorate when exposed to heat, while wet leaves require a longer drying period before storing.

For the best flavor, harvest herbs just before buds open. For seeds, harvest after they have turned from green to brown and before they fall from the plant. For rootstock, harvest in the fall when fully developed.

An early morning herb harvest ensures flavor and fragrance are maximized.

If you plan to dry your herbs, bunch them as you harvest and secure with twine or a rubber band.

DRYING HERBS

Some gardeners claim that dried, summer-grown herbs have a better flavor than herbs grown indoors in winter. Most herbs dry easily and retain their aroma.

It's best to dry herbs in a place that's dark and has good ventilation. Depending on the weather, you may also need to use fans or an air conditioner. Drying screens and bunches can be placed in an attic, around the hot-water heater, or on top of a refrigerator. Dry herbs in the oven on a baking tray. Set the temperature to 100°F (38°C). Stir every 30 minutes for 3–6 hours.

Screens allow air to circulate above and below herbs, such as rosemary, and minimize drying time.

Herb bunches, such as lavender, can take up to two weeks to dry, and are best stored in cool, dark places.

STORING HERBS

The last step in your herb-production process is to store dried foliage, blossoms, roots, or seeds in airtight containers. Or you can freeze them.

For flavorsome, decorative ice cubes, freeze individual herb leaves. Store in freezer bags when set.

Store culinary herbs in clean, dry, glass containers; other materials may affect their chemistry.

Your herbs will store best in glass jars with suction lids or in canning jars with rubber seals. You can also pack them into resealable plastic bags, squeezing out the air before you seal. Crush or strain culinary herbs; use whole leaves and blooms for tea. To freeze herbs en masse, puree with water or oil and pour into ice cube trays.

THE GOOD OIL
Herbs keep well when stored in oil. Place fresh or dried herb leaves in a glass jar, cover with good-quality olive oil, seal, and store in a dark place.

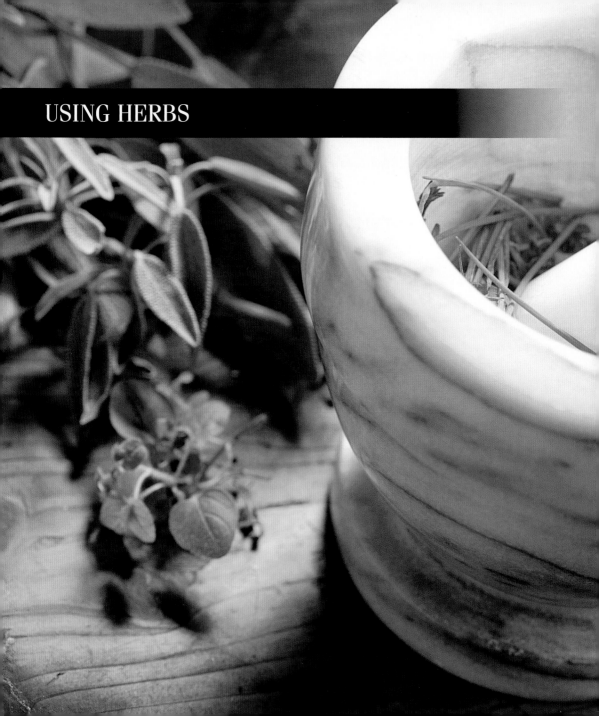

USING HERBS

ESSENTIAL OILS

ESSENTIAL TREATMENTS
Basil: anxiety, headaches
Chamomile: depression, insomnia
Rose: stress, circulation problems,
nausea, headaches
Thyme: indigestion, muscle pain

Essential oils are used in many ways. The scented oils made from your garden will possess some of the same properties as professional essential oils, but not all.

Essential oils must be diluted before being applied to the skin; they are highly toxic when concentrated.

You'll need a lot of plant material to produce your own essential oil as the amount of oil in most herbs is minute. Pack an enamel or glass pan with your herb or herbal blend and cover with vegetable oil. Steep for a day, strain away the plant matter, and repeat the process five times using fresh herbs and the same oil. Store in a tightly sealed glass jar. Use for making potpourris, candles, or soaps.

For a hint of the exotic, add finely ground spices to your scented oil. Mix equal parts cinnamon, cloves, nutmeg, and allspice, or anise, cardamom, and cilantro (coriander).

PRECAUTION: *Avoid using essential oils if you are pregnant or nursing, unless you have the consent and supervision of an obstetrician.*

Essential oil doesn't go off but the carrier oil will; only make up a month's store.

POTPOURRI

A long-lasting and fragrant mix of dried herbs and other crushed plant material, potpourri preserves your favorite summer fragrances year round.

MERELY MALE

For a more masculine scent, start your potpourri with a base of mint, pine, or lemon balm. Rest your homemade potpourri for a month before opening.

MAKING YOUR OWN

You will need a non-metallic bowl, a wooden spoon, about 1 quart (1 liter) of base material, several drops of essential oil, and 1 tablespoon of powdered spice. Mix ingredients together; store in a sealed jar.

BASE MATERIALS

Rose petals, lavender blooms, pine needles, scented geranium leaves, and other aromatic foliage or flowers in plentiful supply are good choices. Gather and dry base materials throughout the season; store in airtight containers until required.

Potpourris are usually on show, so choose attractive material. To enhance the scent, add a few drops of aromatic oil.

Combine herbs to create an enticing aroma theme, such as citrus, floral, woody, or culinary.

HERB SACHETS

Herb sachets and pillows make wonderful gifts. Choose fabrics and colors to match your furnishings or design a shape to fit a theme, such as Valentine's Day.

Gather together squares of colorful fabric cut in any shape or size. Place several tablespoons of crumbled potpourri in the center of each fabric swatch, gather the edges, and tie with ribbon. Use sachets to scent drawers, closets, linen chests, or luggage, or toss them in the tumble dryer to scent your clothing. When they start to lose their scent, gather several in a glass jar and sprinkle lightly with essential oil. Cover and allow to sit for a week before reusing.

> **SWEET DREAMS**
> *Herb-scented pillows were originally a treatment for inducing sleep. Fill your pillow with a blend that suits your needs—lavender for relaxation; citrus for zing.*

Add flourishes, such as dried
lavender sprigs and ribbon
to your aromatic sachets.

HERBAL INSECT REPELLENTS

Herbs were one of the first pest controls used by our ancestors. They work safely to control insects and are easily recycled in compost piles.

Citronella oil is used in insect-repelling candles. Sow citrus-scented herbs to ward off bugs.

INSECT REPELLENT FOR SKIN

1 teaspoon each of essential oils of pennyroyal, citronella, eucalyptus, rosemary, and tansy
1 cup vegetable oil

Shake ingredients together and store away from the light. Rub a small amount between the palms of your hands, then apply to any exposed skin. Avoid contact with eyes. Reapply as necessary. Discontinue use if a rash develops.

SOOTHING HERBS
Dab eucalyptus oil on an insect bite for relief. Alternatively, soak in a bath infused with chamomile leaves or oil.

Plant tansy outside windows and doors; it attracts butterflies and repels pests such as flies and ants.

HERBAL CANDLECRAFT

Candles help to create a refreshing or tranquil atmosphere. Make them as strongly scented as you like and leave in the plant materials for color.

CLEVER CANDLES
Float small herb candles in clear or coloured water and use as a table ornament. Herbal candles in wind-proof containers are perfect for outdoor use.

HERB-SCENTED CANDLES

2 lb (1 kg) paraffin wax, broken into small pieces

2 cups dried herbs or 4 cups fresh herb leaves, blossoms, or woody stems

2 wax crayons or candle colorant

Candle wicking to reach bottom of candle molds

Candle molds or recycled tin cans

Petroleum jelly

Pencils

Melt wax in a bowl over a saucepan of hot water. Stir in the coloring. Remove from the heat and add plant materials. Coat the molds with petroleum jelly. Drop a length of wicking to the bottom of the mold, wrapping the opposite end around a pencil—resting across the top of a mold—to keep the wick centered while pouring in the wax. Set overnight, remove from the mold, and use.

Herbal candles offer variety of color and scent. Press herb flowers to the outside for decoration.

Lavender is a favorite candle scent, along with rosemary. Mix your own blends using herbs from the garden.

BOUQUETS AND WREATHS

Herbal bouquets and wreaths were a special way of communicating long before telephones and email. They are still a lovely way to express yourself.

TUSSIE-MUSSIES

These bouquets are composed of herbs and flowers with different meanings that vary from region to region. In the days of poor sanitation they were held to the nose to disguise offensive odors and were often called nosegays.

WREATHS

Wreaths are an attractive and fragrant way to display your garden wares. Add color or contrast by using different bunches of herbs, dried flowers, or bundles of spices.

Create an aromatic wreath made from herbs grown in your garden. Add fresh or dried flowers to vibrant green foliage.

FLOWERY LANGUAGE
Some herbal blossoms have special meaning.
Iris: *pure heart, courage, faith*
Marigold: *joy, remembrance*
Rose: *love, success*

Herbal homewares—tussie-mussies and wreaths—are a fragrant momento of your flourishing summer garden.

SOAPS AND CLEANSERS

It's simple to make scented soaps and cleansers. For the strongest aroma use herbs such as rosemary, lavender, and thyme—their oils linger on the skin the longest.

HERBAL SOAP

2 teaspoons dried herbs or 2 tablespoons fresh herbs

¼ cup water

Several drops essential oil

2 cups shredded pure soap

In an enamel saucepan, combine herbs, water, and oil and bring to the boil. Simmer for 30 minutes then add the shredded soap, mixing thoroughly. Cool for 15 minutes then mix with your hands. Divide into six parts, roll into balls, and dry on wax paper for two days.

Use lemon-scented herbs for their refreshing fragrance and cleansing properties.

Herbal soaps can soothe sore muscles and invigorate a tired mind. Lavender evokes a sense of calm and relaxation.

HERBAL BEAUTY

People have relied on herbs as beauty treatments for thousands of years. Many of today's commercial lotions are based on herbal ingredients.

Steam treatments make the face perspire, eliminating toxins and increasing circulation, and open pores, which helps the skin absorb the beneficial properties of herbs. Place a handful of fresh or dried herbs in a bowl, pour over boiling water, and use a towel to make a tent. Steam your face for 10–15 minutes. Rinse with cool water, or use the following toner. Add two handfuls of lavender flowers to 1 pint (500 ml) of cider vinegar. Infuse for two weeks. Strain, add 2 pints (1 L) of water, bottle, and seal.

FRUITFUL REFRESHMENT
An ancient beauty treatment for the face is a mask of freshly pulped strawberries. Apply, avoiding the eye area, leave for 30 minutes, then remove.

Fragrant lavender is a popular ingredient in beauty products. It helps the healing process.

After a hard day's work, try a herbal foot bath to aid relaxation. Add sage, thyme, or lavender leaves to hot water.

HERBAL DYES

Herbs have been used to dye cloth for thousands of years. Until the 19th century, when the chemical industry developed, all dyes were natural.

While chemical dyes offer a wider range of colors, plant dyes are unsurpassed for richness and subtlety of hue. They are created by boiling fresh or dried plant parts in water, and then adding fabric.

Natural fibers such as cotton, linen, silk, and wool are simple to dye at home using your own herbs, vegetables, flowers, and wild plant materials.

HERBS TO DYE FOR

Brown: walnut husks and shells, juniper berries, tea leaves

Orange: onion skins, turmeric, bloodroot root

Yellow: safflower, tansy, chamomile, agrimony flowers

Blue: elder berries, cornflowers

Beige: St John's wort flowers, blackberry shoots

Red: madder roots, lady's bedstraw roots, oregano

Pink: sorrel or lady's bedstraw roots

Green: nettle plant, hyssop or elder leaves

Wool is the easiest natural fiber to dye.
Use homegrown herbs, vegetables,
and flowers to create unique tones.

MEDICINAL HERBS

Compared with the precision of modern-day medicine, herbal remedies can seem old-fashioned. But many of today's medicines were derived from plants.

Herbs are the oldest form of medicine in the world and have been used for centuries.

In most cultures around the world, the earliest forms of healing were based on herbs and that knowledge was handed down to each new generation. Written records show herbal medicines date back to 3000 BC in Egypt, China, Babylon, and India. In many countries, herbal remedies are still the only readily available treatment.

Use separate mortar and pestles when preparing medicinal and culinary herbs.

Many herbs are used for healing but should only be taken under professional guidance.

FAVORITE MEDICINAL HERBS

In the past, people relied on many different herbal medicines. Willowbark, for example, helped relieve headaches while iris root treated toothaches.

To treat cold and flu symptoms, make an infusion from rosehips; drink one cup three times a day.

Use the following as a quick reference to some of the more common and beneficial medicinal herbs and their soothing and healing properties. Before using any herbal remedy, it is wise to take advice from a qualified practitioner or doctor.

CALMING CHAMOMILE
Like catmint, chamomile will relieve cramps, settle upset stomachs, and aid digestion. Make an infusion from the flowers and drink three cups daily.

Passionflower tea can have a tranquilizing effect on the central nervous system.

Make a decoction from witch hazel bark and use it in a compress for cuts, bruises, and insect bites.

FAVORITE MEDICINAL HERBS

Rosemary: Make an infusion from the leaves and flowers, and drink three times daily for stomach upsets. Use the infusion as a rinse after shampooing and conditioning hair.

Rosemary and sage are wonderful medicinal herbs, treating a variety of ailments, from nausea to cuts.

Sage: Use crushed, fresh leaves as a preliminary antiseptic on minor wounds. An infusion of sage leaves aids digestion and may also reduce perspiration.

Thyme: For cold, flu, and allergy relief, make an infusion from the leaves and stems, and drink three times daily.

POTENT PEPPERMINT
Peppermint is wonderful as a decongestant and for settling an upset stomach. Make an infusion from the leaves and drink three cups daily. Pregnant women should avoid peppermint.

A tea made from fresh coneflower (echinacea) roots treats respiratory infections. Drink up to three cups a day.

To promote healing, apply the fresh gel from aloe leaves to scalds, sunburn, blisters, acne, and scrapes.

Make a compress from calendula flowers and apply to stings, bruises, scrapes, and burns.

HERBAL REMEDIES

Prepare herbal remedies, such as teas, infusions, syrups, compresses, poultices, and ointments from your herb harvest to treat a number of common ailments.

CHOOSING YOUR HERBS
Refer to Favorite Medicinal Herbs, *page 74, for suggested herbal remedies. Be sure to obtain professional guidance regarding preparation and dosages.*

Infusions are made by pouring boiling water over herb leaves or flowers and steeping them for up to 15 minutes. They are a good way of making herbal remedies at home and are best drunk fresh, while still hot, although they can be stored in the refrigerator for a day or two. Dilute to taste or sweeten with honey or fruit juice.

To ensure your herbal remedies are of the highest quality and purity, use plants grown in your garden.

Herbal teas are often used to remedy common ailments. The difference between an infusion and a tea is the length of time the herbs are allowed to steep. For more information, turn to page 96.

HERBAL REMEDIES

COMPRESSES

Prepare an infusion, then soak a towel in the warm liquid. Wring out and lay it upon the affected area, covering with a dry towel. As the compress cools, replace it with a warm one. Continue for 30 minutes.

POULTICE

Poultices are used to treat infection and relieve muscle aches.

¼ cup dried herbs or 3 cups of fresh herbs, washed, dried, and minced

4 cups oatmeal

Mix the herbs and oatmeal with hot water to form a paste. Place paste directly onto the skin and cover with a towel. Replace when cool. Continue treatment for 30 minutes.

Try a lavender compress to relieve tension, or a garlic or ginger compress to treat nasal and chest congestion.

Use muslin-wrapped herbal stamps, which are filled with a poultice, in aromatherapy massage.

THERAPEUTIC OILS

There are hundreds of essential oils to choose from, but a basic few, kept on hand, will more than suffice for therapeutic use.

COMMON THERAPEUTIC OILS

Lavender oil is a natural antibiotic, antiseptic, antidepressant, and sedative.

Peppermint oil is very useful in treating digestive disorders. Do not use during pregnancy.

Chamomile oil is helpful in treating anxiety, but should never be used by people with low blood pressure.

Geranium oil works mostly on the emotions. Mixed with massage oil, it is used to treat acne, dermatitis, and eczema.

Rosemary oil treats headaches, muscle pain, and dandruff.

THE PURITY TEST
For effective therapy, only pure essential oils should be used. When dropped on blotting paper, they impregnate it, then evaporate leaving no oily patch.

Diffusers are especially made to heat essential oils in order to release their aroma.

When buying products containing essential oils, go to health-food stores rather than stores that sell cosmetics.

AROMATHERAPY

Literally "therapy by smell", aromatherapy uses the fragrant, natural essential oils of herbs and flowers to beneficial effect on the body.

Each herb releases different scent molecules that are detected by the olfactory nerves in the nose. These nerves are linked with the areas of the brain that deal with emotions, memory, and creativity. As a response, the brain injects particular chemicals into the body; in turn this can affect the workings of bodily functions.

By mixing two or more essential oils you can create an aroma that has added therapeutic properties. However, it is important to get the ratio right. Consult a professional for recommended combinations.

HEADY AROMA
You can release the aromas of essential oils in many ways. Try adding them to water in a humidifier, or place a drop on a log before popping it on the fire.

Scent sticks are steeped in essential oils and release fragrant aromas that aid in healing and relaxation.

Herbal joss sticks have been used for centuries to cleanse the air during religious ceremonies. Use them at home to create a mood.

COOKING WITH HERBS

If you want to learn how to use culinary herbs, grow them. A bushy, fragrant herb plant just outside the kitchen door is the best inspiration for culinary success.

FROM LITTLE THINGS
Growing just a few of the classics can give you endless culinary options. Bunch different herbs together for use in tasty soups, stews, and sauces.

If you've never used fresh herbs, start by following simple recipes that appeal to you. Most cookbooks offer a variety of dishes that require herbs for flavoring.

Another way to become familiar with herbs is to add them to food you already cook. Add snippets of fresh herbs to scrambled eggs, trying a new herb each time. Once you've developed preferences for certain herbs, combine them with others in the same dish.

Culinary herbs should be used sparingly, to enhance the natural flavors of the other ingredients. Most herbs should be added at the end of a recipe; their flavors are released with gentle heat, but lost if cooked for more than 30 minutes.

Create unique flavors by combining herbs such as rosemary, bay leaf, Italian parsley, garlic, pepper, and salt.

A sharp kitchen knife is a must for mincing herbs. Rub leaves between your hands before processing to release their aromatic essential oils.

USING FRESH AND DRIED HERBS

You can substitute fresh for dried herbs in most recipes. Since fresh herbs contain more water, use two to three times more fresh herbs than the dried measurement.

Fresh herbs are a great addition to salads. Add chopped or whole sprigs of basil, chervil, chives, dill, oregano, thyme, tarragon, or whatever flavors you enjoy. Use blossoms from chives, borage, and rosemary to garnish the finished salad. Or wrap pate or softened cream-cheese bundles in fresh leaves such as nasturtium.

THE DAILY GRIND

If you don't have a mortar and pestle, use your coffee machine to grind herbs. For the best flavor, use ground herbs immediately. Freeze leftovers in airtight bags.

Coat your favourite cheese in dried or freshly ground herbs, or add a sprig for color and flavor.

Use a mezzaluna to cut fresh or dried herbs such as rosemary, basil, and thyme. Add whole bay leaves to your cooking, but remove before serving.

HERB BUTTERS

Herb butters are colorful and fragrant spreads for warm biscuits, bread, vegetables, or meat. Add a dab to pasta or rice, or use to baste grilled or baked fish.

BUTTER ME UP
Pack herb butter into molds; form spheres with a melon-baller; shave curls from chilled butter with a sharp knife. Wrap in plastic and refrigerate for up to a month.

Parsley is the herb most commonly used in herb butters, but there are plenty of alternatives. Experiment with basil, tarragon, or a combination of others. Choose herbs that will complement the food being served. Mint butter melting over hot potatoes is delicious. Let the butter soften at room temperature, then beat in the herbs and other seasonings by hand or with an electric mixer. To maximize the flavor, chill for at least three hours before serving.

Make butter when your herbs are plentiful for maximum flavor, and store in the freezer for up to three months.

Wash herbs carefully before adding them to butter; soil and grit can be concealed in the small folds of leaves.

HERBAL VINEGARS

You can use herbal vinegars in most recipes that call for vinegar, including sauces, marinades, and stews. Make your own and experiment with flavors.

Simply pack a bottle with fresh herbs then fill with vinegar, or heat the vinegar to almost boiling—warm vinegar releases the herbs' essential oils faster. Try combining several herbs to create your own special blend. Garlic and chives work well with most of the strongly flavored herbs, such as basil, dill, and thyme. Mix equal parts of parsley, thyme, and rosemary for a special concoction.

Add fresh herbs to vinegar for flavor and visual appeal.

For ease of identification, label your homemade vinegars. Recycled wine or ketchup bottles make good containers.

OILS AND DRESSINGS

Grab a handful of herbs from your garden and create homemade oils and dressings whenever you want to add extra flavor to your cooking.

Use flavored oils wherever a recipe calls for oil in marinades and sauces, or make your salad dressings and halve the oil content to limit calories. Add any single herb or combination that suits your menu. Extra virgin olive oil or sesame oil are best, but other oils such as safflower, macadamia, and walnut work well too. Be sure to label your bottles.

> **SALTING HERBS**
> Herb salt—a mix of sea salt and fresh or dried herbs—can add instant flavor to food, and has the associated health benefit of reducing your pure-salt intake.

For a simple dressing with extra tang, combine minced herbs, Greek yoghurt, and lemon juice.

Garlic gives oil a rich flavor; add a whole clove for extra punch. Try it on pasta, vegetables, or red meat.

HERBAL TEAS

Made from aromatic leaves, flowers, or roots steeped in boiling water, tea is an ancient drink. Herbal teas don't have to be medicinal to be enjoyed.

Start with herbs that have similar flavors, such as mint, sage, and chamomile. Use 1 teaspoon of fresh leaves for each cup (250 ml) of boiling water. Pour water over the herb in a china or glass pot (metals, including stainless steel, can change the flavor of some herbs). Steep for 4–6 minutes for the best flavor. Herbal tea should be lightly colored and mild. A strong tea will be bitter and might cause unexpected side effects if the herb has medicinal properties.

WHICH TEA TO CHOOSE?
Peppermint tea is highly refreshing; dried chicory roots are used as a coffee substitute; rosehip tea is high in vitamin C; nettle tea stimulates digestion.

Dry and infuse chamomile flowers to make a soothing tea that has a sweet, apple-like scent.

Herb leaves and blossoms intended for tea should be used fresh, or left whole, dried, and stored.

HERBAL SWEETS

Herbal sweets are simple to prepare and make attractive gifts. Surprise loved ones with jars of herb-flavored honeys or baskets of candied flowers.

Candied borage and lavender blooms add both color and pizzazz to dainty cupcakes, and are also edible.

HERB-FLAVORED HONEYS

Use instead of sugar in drinks and recipes, or as a sweet spread. Use any herb singularly or combine a few. Try anise seed, cilantro (coriander), lavender, lemon verbena, thyme, marjoram, mint, or rosemary.

CANDIED FLOWERS

Edible blossoms are a treat usually limited to the growing season. Preserve petals with sugar and they'll last up to six months.

BLOOMING SWEETIES
To make candied herb blossoms, beat an egg white until frothy, coat the petals in it, and sprinkle them with sugar. Dry on waxed paper for two days.

Rose-petal honey is a tasty topping for toast and a comforting addition to tea.

Flavor decadent chocolate truffles with a sprinkling of cinnamon, cardamom, and cloves.

GUIDE TO HERBS

FULL SUN

PART SHADE

POT SUITABLE

USE AS A TEA

CULINARY USES

ESSENTIAL OIL

Achillea millefolium
YARROW

Displaying delicate, ferny foliage and long-lasting flowers, yarrow is an easy-to-grow herb and a welcome addition to ornamental beds and gardens.

Ideal soil *Fertile, well-drained.*
Parts used *Whole plant.*
Pests/diseases *Flowers attract aphid-eating insects.*
Medicinal *Colds, influenza, arthritis; as anticoagulant.*

GROWING GUIDELINES

Sow seed shallowly indoors in early spring or outdoors in late spring. Divide large clumps in spring and fall.

Growth habit Perennial; height to 3 feet (90 cm).
Flowers Summer; tiny white, pink, or red florets.

HARVESTING AND STORING

Pick flowers with plenty of stem; strip foliage before hanging in bunches to dry. Holds color well.

Add a finely chopped yarrow leaf to a wheelbarrow of garden compost to speed the process of decomposition.

Cut blossoms last well in water. They're also used to make yellow or olive dye.

Yarrow flowers attract beneficial insects. To promote growth, pick the pungent blossoms often.

Agastache foeniculum

ANISE HYSSOP

Similar in appearance to mint, with square stems and attractive lavender blossoms, the leaves of this pretty herb have a distinctive licorice scent.

Ideal soil Rich, well drained.
Parts used Leaves, flowers.
Medicinal Colds, coughs, nausea; as appetite enhancer.
Culinary In salads; as a tea, seasoning for meat.

Thrives in a sheltered, sunny spot. Tall plants may need staking.

GROWING GUIDELINES

Sow seed shallowly outside in the spring.
Growth habit Perennial; height to 3 feet (90 cm).
Flowers Midsummer to fall; spiked mauve blossoms.

HARVESTING AND STORING

Harvest leaves during summer. For foliage and blooms, cut whole plant after flowering. Hang to dry.

Anise hyssop flowers attract bees and other beneficial insects. The leaves have a licorice-like flavor.

Also known as church steeples, sticklewort, or cocklebur, agrimony adds height and color to gardens.

Agrimonia eupatoria

AGRIMONY

This easy-to-grow, aromatic herb has hairy, dark-green foliage and yellow blossoms. It is most commonly used as a tea and gargle for sore throats.

Ideal soil Light, well-drained.
Parts used Whole plant.
Pests/diseases Powdery mildew.
Medicinal Food allergies, sore throats, diarrhea, cystitis.
Culinary As a tea.

GROWING GUIDELINES

Sow seed outdoors or divide older plants in spring. Self-sows each year, .
Growth habit Perennial; height 2–3 feet (60–90 cm).
Flowers Summer; tall spikes with lightly scented flowers then bristly fruits.

HARVESTING AND STORING

Collect foliage just before flowers bloom. Strip leaves and spread to dry or hang in bunches. Lift root at end of season; dry. Store in airtight containers.

All parts of the plant—root, stem, leaf, flower, and fruit—are used for medicinal purposes.

107

To maximize bulb size, prune garlic's star-shaped blossoms as they appear in early summer.

Allium sativum

GARLIC

One of the world's most familiar herbs, garlic is used to flavor food from almost every ethnic cuisine. It is also an excellent insect-repelling plant.

GROWING GUIDELINES

Separate individual cloves from the bulb and plant in late fall. Side dress with compost in early spring; don't plant after applications of fresh manure.

Growth habit Perennial bulb; height to 2 feet (60 cm).

Flowers Early summer; small, white to pinkish blossoms.

Ideal soil *Deep, well-drained.*
Parts used *Bulbs.*
Medicinal *Colds, infections, skin problems, dysentery.*
Culinary *With meat, seafood, vegetables; in sauces.*

Garlic's optimum storage container is its self-contained, neatly-wrapped bulb.

Plant large garlic cloves to produce healthy plants, and don't overwater; it may cause bulb disease.

HARVESTING AND STORING

Dig bulbs after tops have died down and before skins begin to decay underground. Place in a single layer in a shaded spot to dry, then cut away tops leaving about 2 inches (5 cm) of stem. Hang loose bulbs in nets from the ceiling.

YIELD AND TIMING

A 20-foot (6-m) row produces 5–10 pounds (2.5–5 kg) of garlic. Timing the harvest can be tricky. Too early and bulbs are small; too late and the outer skin may tear, making the bulbs store poorly. Check the status of one head before you harvest the rest.

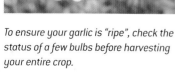

To ensure your garlic is "ripe", check the status of a few bulbs before harvesting your entire crop.

Wrap twine around garlic stems, or plait the tops of freshly dug plants, and hang to dry in a dark place.

Allium schoenoprasum

CHIVES

The graceful leaves and blossoms of chives have a mild onion flavor, especially when used fresh. Add leaves to cooking; toss the flowers in salads or use as a garnish.

Ideal soil Rich, well-drained.
Parts used Whole plant.
Pests/diseases Bulb diseases.
Medicinal Stimulates appetite, aids digestion.
Culinary For flavoring; in salads.

GROWING GUIDELINES

Sow seed indoors in late winter and transplant in early spring, or sow outside in spring.
Growth habit Perennial bulb; height to 12 inches (30 cm).
Flowers Summer; pink, or lavender to purple globular flowers.

HARVESTING AND STORING

Use fresh leaf tips in summer. Pick flowers soon after opening. Leaves and flowers can be frozen.

The delicate flavor of chives is lost soon after harvesting, so use them fresh, or chop and dry.

Chives ward off pests and are recommended companion plants for roses, carrots, and tomatoes.

Aloe vera barbadensis [A. vera]

ALOE

For color and contrast, grow several of the more than 300 species of succulent aloe. The leaves contain a soothing gel, which is used to treat skin problems.

Aloe rarely flowers in cool climates; in warmer areas it produces striking blooms atop a towering stalk.

Ideal soil Well-drained.
Parts used Sap, leaves from plants at least two years old.
Pests/diseases Mealybugs.
Precaution Not suitable for pregnant woman, or people with haemorrhoids.

GROWING GUIDELINES

Divide in spring from established plants; dry for two days before planting in pots. Mix coarse sand with potting compost. Winter indoors.

Growth habit Perennial; height to 3 feet (90 cm).

Flowers Summer; tubular, yellow to red flowers.

HARVESTING AND STORING

Cut leaves for gel as needed; remove outer leaves first. Store in the refrigerator.

Grow aloe on a sunny windowsill in the kitchen or bathroom, and avoid excess watering.

Tubular aloe flowers come in a variety of colours, from canary yellow to tangerine and ruby.

MEDICINAL USES

For burns, sunburn, cuts, dermatitis, eczema, constipation, poor appetite, and digestive problems. Has anti-inflammatory properties and aids healing. Also used to prevent nail biting.

GARDENERS' TRIVIA

Historically, aloe was used for embalming. Christian records show that the body of Jesus was wrapped in a cloth that had been impregnated with aloe and myrrh. It has also been identified in ancient Egyptian wall paintings, and was reputed to be one of Cleopatra's secret beauty ingredients.

Aloe gel is used in pharmaceutical preparations, facial creams, cosmetics, and to make a violet dye. The plant is also known as the first-aid or healing herb.

Propagate clump-forming aloe by division; the impressive but impotent flowers rarely form seeds.

Lemon-scented verbena leaves are used in herbal teas and also dried for use in potpourri.

Aloysia triphylla

LEMON VERBENA

Grown for its strong lemon aroma and flavor, this herb is well worth the extra care required. It is often used in teas and cosmetics.

GROWING GUIDELINES

In cold areas, place pots outdoors in summer and indoors in winter. Feed with compost tea regularly. Pinch tips to encourage bushy growth. Prune in fall.

Growth habit Perennial; height 5–10 feet (1.5–3 m).

Flowers Late summer; tiny white to lavender blossoms.

HARVESTING AND STORING

Snip leaves or cut foliage back by half in summer and fall. Dry in a cool, shady spot.

Lemon verbena will train as a mop-headed standard.

Ideal soil *Light, well-drained.*
Parts used *Leaves, oil.*
Medicinal *Colds, flatulence, stomach cramps, indigestion.*
Culinary *Salads, tea, stuffing.*

Alpinia galanga
GALANGAL

Members of the same family as ginger, with which they have much in common both in form and flavor, the tropical galangals are a popular ingredient in Asian dishes.

> *Ideal soil* Well-drained, humusy.
> *Parts used* Rhizomes, oil.
> *Pests/diseases* Red spider mite.
> *Medicinal* Gum or skin infections.
> *Culinary* Rhizomes for ginger-like flavor. Oil in liqueurs, soft drinks.

GROWING GUIDELINES

Propagate by rhizome division as new growth appears.
Growth habit Perennial; height to 6 feet (1.8 m).
Flowers Year round; small white blossoms.

HARVESTING AND STORING

Roots of plants 3–6 years old are lifted and used raw, dried, or distilled for oil. Store fresh root in an airtight container.

Dried galangal root is used in Indonesian, Thai, and Malaysian cuisine for its ginger-like flavor.

A drink made from sliced galangal and lime juice is taken as a tonic in Southeast Asia.

In some countries, galangal root is worn by children as a charm to protect them from evil spirits.

Althaea officinalis

MARSH MALLOW

Add marsh mallow leaves to salads, or slice and cook the roots like potatoes. The roots were originally used to produce the consistency typical of the confection marshmallow.

Ideal soil Light, damp.
Parts used Leaves, flowers, roots.
Medicinal Infusion of leaves as gargle for sore throat, as a drink for bronchial and gastric issues. Grated root as a skin ointment.

GROWING GUIDELINES

Sow seed shallowly outdoors in spring; divide clumps or take basal cuttings from foliage or roots in fall.

Growing habit Perennial; height to 4 feet (1.2 m).

Flowers Late summer to early fall; pink or blue-white blooms.

HARVESTING AND STORING

Harvest leaves just before flowering. Collect and dry flowers at their peak. Dig roots in the fall from plants that are at least two years old; scrub and boil or slice before drying.

This hardy herb thrives in moist places, such as salt marshes. Its peeled root was traditionally given to babies as a teething aid.

Marsh mallow is easily identified by its large flowers and soft, velvety, lobed leaves.

The entire dill plant is aromatic,
from its flowers and seeds to
its carrot-like taproot.

Anethum graveolens

DILL

Dill makes an attractive background in garden beds. In American history, dill seed was given to children to induce sleep during long Sunday sermons.

Move potted dill around the garden to lure beneficial insects and bugs.

> *Ideal soil* Well-drained, rich.
> *Parts used* Leaves, seeds, oils.
> *Medicinal* Nausea, excessive wind and hiccups, colic.
> *Culinary* Potato, seafood, eggs.

GROWING GUIDELINES

Sow seeds shallowly in spring. Water well. Prefers sunny spot.

Growing habit Annual; height 2–3 feet (60–90 cm).

Flowers Summer; aromatic, yellow flowers.

HARVESTING AND STORING

Clip fresh leaves as needed. Freeze whole or chopped; dry on nonmetallic screens. Collect flower heads before seeds mature and fall. Store seeds in an airtight container for up to a year.

Fresh leaves retain their flavor for a week if refrigerated, and are a tasty addition to dressings and vinegar.

Angelica archangelica

EUROPEAN ANGELICA

This sweet-scented herb resembles its close relatives, parsley and cilantro (coriander). Its leaf stems can be candied and its roots infused to make a tea.

Ideal soil Rich, cool, moist.
Parts used All, except flowers.
Medicinal Digestive problems, anorexia, rheumatism, migraines.
Precaution Not given to pregnant women or diabetics.

GROWING GUIDELINES

When sewing, press lightly into soil surface and leave uncovered. Sow fresh summer seed as soon as it ripens.
Growth habit Biennial; height 5–8 feet (1.5–2.4 m).
Flowers Summer; tiny, honey-scented blossoms.

HARVESTING AND STORING

Collect small stalks the first summer; harvest roots in fall. Pick stems and leaves in the second spring. Harvest ripe seeds before they fall; dry and store.

Leaves are cooked like spinach and eaten as a vegetable, while their stems are stewed to make jam.

Angelica's name is derived from the medieval belief that it would ward off evil and cure all ills. Today, its seeds are used to flavor drinks.

Anthriscus cerefolium
CHERVIL

Reputed to improve memory and aid depression, Chervil grows best and retains more flavor when temperatures are cool in summer.

Chervil is best used fresh. Minimize flavor lose by storing in glass jars and adding to recipes at the end.

> *Ideal soil* Moist, well-drained.
> *Parts used* Leaves.
> *Medicinal* Jaundice, eczema, conjunctivitis, rheumatism.
> *Culinary* Potato, fish, egg dishes.

GROWING GUIDELINES

Sow fresh seed shallowly outdoors in early spring or undercover in fall. Keep seedlings moist. Transplants poorly.
Growth habit Annual; height 1–2 feet (30–60 cm).
Flowers Summer; small, umbrella-like white clusters.

HARVESTING AND STORING

Snip off leaves continuously as required after 6–8 weeks of growth.

Chervil has an aroma similar to aniseed and parsley combined, and is used in soups and salads.

Chervil has delicate, fern-like leaves and dainty flowers, and grows well below plants that offer some shade.

Wild celery flourishes in damp, protected sites. Its seeds are used sparingly to flavor curries.

Apium graveolens
WILD CELERY

Wild celery has been used as a food and medicinal plant since earliest times and was found in Tutankhamun's tomb. Cultivated celery is more frequently used today.

> *Ideal soil* Rich, moist.
> *Parts used* Whole plant.
> *Pests/diseases* Mosaic virus, slugs, celery-fly maggots.
> *Medicinal* Gout, fungal infections, indigestion, rheumatoid arthritis.

GROWING GUIDELINES

Sow seed in early spring Keep well weeded and watered. Apply compost tea monthly.
Growth habit Perennial; height 1–3 feet (30–90 cm).
Flowers Late summer; tiny, green-white clusters.

HARVESTING AND STORING

In fall, harvest fleshy, bulbous roots and use fresh or dried in tinctures. Collect seeds as they ripen.

Wild celery is rarely used in cooking. It is toxic in large doses.

Arctium lappa

BURDOCK

This colorful herb has large, woolly leaves, thistle-like flowers, and an edible root. When ingested, the seeds have been proven to lower blood sugar levels.

Ideal soil Deep, loose, moist.
Parts used Stems, roots, seeds.
Medicinal Skin problems, rheumatism, colds.
Culinary Stalks and roots as vegetable. Roots as a tea.

GROWING GUIDELINES

Sow seed shallowly in early spring or fall. Deep taproot makes transplanting difficult. Self-sows.

Growth habit Biennial; height to 5 feet (1.5 m).
Flowers Summer; purple to red, prickly blossoms.

HARVESTING AND STORING

Harvest young, edible leaf stalks in spring and summer. Lift, scrub, and slice roots at season's end. Dry on paper in sun. Store in airtight containers.

Also known as lappa, gobo, cuckold, or beggar's buttons, burdock thrives in full sun and tolerates part shade.

Burdock flowers mature to burr-like seedheads that cling to passers-by. Seeds are used to treat pneumonia.

Armoracia rusticana
HORSERADISH

Horseradish is a weedy herb with a perennial root. Originally cultivated as a medicinal plant, today it is used mainly as a culinary herb. Its sharp taste adds flavor to roast beef.

GROWING GUIDELINES

Plant straight, young roots horizontally in spring.
Growth habit Perennial; height 1–4 feet (30–120 cm).
Flowers Early summer; small, white blossoms.

HARVESTING AND STORING

Harvest roots in fall. Scrub before storing in refrigerator, or pack in damp sand for planting. Pick leaves as needed.

Ideal soil Fertile, well-drained.
Parts used Leaves, roots.
Medicinal Gout, urinary infections, arthritis, wounds.
Culinary Leaves for salads; root to flavor fish, vinegar, roast beef.

Horseradish is grown mainly for its large, pungently spicy roots.

Delicate summer flowers fail to produce viable seeds. Leaves can be used in salads and sandwiches.

Arnica montana
ARNICA

Arnica is a hardy herb with several flower stalks. An ointment to soothe sprains, aching muscles, and bruises can be made using the blooms.

GROWING GUIDELINES

Propagate by division or sow seed indoors in early spring. Transplant outdoors after frosts have passed.
Growth habit Perennial; height to 2 feet (60 cm).
Flowers Midsummer; yellow to orange, daisy-like blooms.

HARVESTING AND STORING

Cut flowers when fully open. Dry. Lift roots in fall after leaves have dried.

Mix arnica flowers with vegetable oil or lard to make an ointment that soothes sore muscles.

Arnica loves regular watering but will flower in drier conditions. It is also known as mountain tobacco.

Artemisia dracunculus

FRENCH TARRAGON

Tarragon's heavy licorice flavor holds well, making it an extremely useful herb in the kitchen. It used to be known as a dragon herb, hence the species name.

Ideal soil Well-drained.
Parts used Leaves, oil.
Medicinal Indigestion, worms, toothache, rheumatism.
Precaution Not suitable for pregnant women.

GROWING GUIDELINES

Seldom sets seed. Take cuttings of new summer growth. Divide older plants in spring or fall every three years.

Growth habit Hardy perennial; height 2–4 feet (60–120 cm).

Flowers Summer, in warm climates; small, greenish-yellow blossoms.

HARVESTING AND STORING

Cut summer foliage as required; store in the refrigerator wrapped in paper towel, then placed in a plastic bag. Hang to dry away from sunlight; store in airtight containers.

French tarragon was originally used externally as a poultice to treat poisonous stings and bites.

Tarragon is a tasty addition to chicken and egg dishes, but use sparingly—the flavor is very strong.

Smell before you buy as the licorice scent only exists in the French variety; its leaves are a flavorsome addition to vinegar.

Mugwort leaf is used in traditional Chinese medicine on the skin at acupuncture points.

Artemisia vulgaris

MUGWORT

Mugwort is an appealing ornamental for both the garden and floral wreaths. The leaves have a similar scent to sage and are said to repel insects.

> **Ideal soil** Light, well-drained.
> **Parts used** Leaves.
> **Medicinal** Depression, worms, menstrual problems, fungal wash.
> **Precaution** Not suitable for pregnant women.

GROWING GUIDELINES

Sow seed outdoors after frosts have passed. Divide older plants in spring or fall.

Growth habit Perennial; height 3–6 feet (90–180 cm).

Flowers Late summer; reddish-brown or yellow, ball-shaped blossoms.

HARVESTING AND STORING

Collect leaves just before flowering in summer. Dry and store in airtight containers.

New leaf growth on flowering stems differs from mature mugwort leaves—the former are more elongate and have downy, white undersides.

Berberis vulgaris
BARBERRY

This woody, ornamental shrub makes an excellent hedge and is easily trained to twist and turn in knot gardens. It also has anti-cancer properties.

Soil Moist, fertile, well-drained.
Parts used Leaves, bark, roots, and fruits.
Medicinal Gallstones, dysentery.
Precaution Not suitable for pregnant women.

GROWING GUIDELINES

Sow seed outdoors in spring or fall. Take cuttings in late summer. Prune branches after flowering.
Growth habit Deciduous; height to 8 feet (2.4 m).
Flowers Spring; yellow blooms, then berries.

HARVESTING AND STORING

Collect berries in fall and use fresh. Lift roots in summer or fall; shave into slices. Strip bark anytime, then dry thoroughly. Store in airtight containers.

Barberry's fruit is its only edible component. It was once used in jelly for meat dishes.

Barberry bark is used to make a yellow dye. The robust shrub quickly becomes overgrown if neglected.

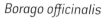

Borago officinalis
BORAGE

This bristly plant, with drooping clusters of brightly colored blooms, attracts honeybees. Its leaves have a cucumber flavor and are used in salads.

Ideal soil Rich, well-drained.
Parts used Leaves, flowers, seeds, oil.
Medicinal Bronchial and throat infections, skin problems.
Culinary Flowers are candied.

GROWING GUIDELINES

Sow seeds outdoors after frosts have passed. Self-sows.
Growth habit Annual: height 1–2 feet (30–60 cm).
Flowers Midsummer; pink, purple, or blue blossoms.

HARVESTING AND STORING

Harvest foliage anytime; use fresh. Cut flowers just after opening and use fresh, or dry for floral arrangements.

Historically, borage was used to give people courage.

Borage blossoms have five narrow, triangular petals that turn pink with age. The herb is an excellent companion plant for strawberries.

Brassica spp.

MUSTARD

Most mustards are annuals or biennials. Some are "winter annuals" that remain green even when buried in snow. Mustard is a great pest deterrent.

Mustard seeds have a sharp, bitter taste. White seeds are used for pickling; black and brown in curries.

GROWING GUIDELINES

Sow seed shallowly outdoors from early spring to fall. Prepare beds with compost or well-rotted manure.
Growth habit Annual/biennial; height 4–6 feet (1.2–1.8 m).
Flowers Summer; four-petalled, yellow blossoms.

Ideal soil Fertile, well-drained.
Parts used Leaves, flowers, oil, and seeds.
Medicinal In baths for muscle pain, respiratory tract infections, and rheumatism.

HARVESTING AND STORING

Cut whole plant 10 days after sowing, or pick single leaves from older plants. Harvest flowers on opening. Collect ripe seeds; dry or infuse in vinegar.

For the mildest flavor, pick young mustard leaves in the morning.

Mustard flowers are used as a garnish for salads; young leaves can be cooked as a vegetable.

Calendula oil is made from the brightest orange petals and has antiseptic properties.

Calendula officinalis

CALENDULA

Calendula is a cheery, dependable bloomer in the garden. It is one of the most versatile herbs, with cosmetic, culinary, and medicinal uses.

GROWING GUIDELINES

Sow seed outdoors in fall or spring. Pinch away old blooms for continuous flowering.

Growth habit Annual: height 1–2 feet (30–60 cm).

Flowers Summer; golden-yellow to orange blossoms.

HARVESTING AND STORING

Dry petals in shade on paper; store in moisture-proof containers. Preserve whole flowers in vinegar.

Dried petals are used as a saffron substitute in rice and soups, or infused to color butter and cakes.

Soil: Well-drained.
Parts used: Flower petals.
Medicinal: Gastrointestinal infection, eczema, athlete's foot.
Precaution: Not suitable for pregnant women.

Infuse calendula petals for tea; add whole flowers to salads or preserve in vinegar.

149

Capparis spinosa

CAPER

Capers are the tiny, unopened, green flower buds of a spiny shrub native to southern Europe and North Africa. They have been used in regional cooking for centuries.

GROWING GUIDELINES

Propagate by ripe wood cuttings in summer.
Growth habit Prostrate shrub; height 3–6 feet (90–180 cm).
Flowers Summer to early fall; white to pink blossoms.

HARVESTING AND STORING

Pick flower buds in the early morning. Strip bark from roots in fall; dry.

Capers have an affinity with garlic, lemon, anchovies, and olives, and have a "goaty" taste.

Soil Sandy, well-drained.
Parts used Root bark, buds.
Medicinal Gastrointestinal infections, gout, coughs.
Culinary In Mediterranean cuisine; reduces food oiliness.

Pick flower buds in the early morning and pickle in salt or white vinegar. The finest capers are round and hard.

Capsicum annuum
PEPPER

Peppers are rich in vitamin C. The fruit is crisp and juicy when green, but sweeter when allowed to ripen, and is used to treat asthma, coughs, and fevers.

Delicate pepper blossoms attract beneficial insects to the garden; pests tend to avoid spicy plants.

GROWING GUIDELINES

Sow seed in spring. Apply tomato fertilizer on flowering.
Growth habit Perennial; height 1–2 feet (30–60 cm).
Flowers Summer; white blooms, then red, yellow, or orange fruit.

HARVESTING AND STORING

Pick green peppers when large enough to use. Pick ripe peppers when 75 per cent colored; they'll finish ripening at room temperature. Use fresh within two weeks, or freeze or pickle.

Soil *Light, well-drained.*
Parts used *Fruit.*
Pests/diseases *Powdery mildew.*
Medicinal *Sprains, chilblains, digestive problems, laryngitis.*
Culinary *As vegetable; in salads.*

Use fresh peppers as a vegetable, and in pickles, chutneys, and salads.

Ripe fruit is dried to make cayenne pepper, chilli powder, and paprika. Contact can cause eye irritation.

Carthamus tinctorius

SAFFLOWER

The orange-yellow blossoms of safflower are used to produce yellow and red dyes, which are used in rouge. The seeds are used to make cooking oil.

Soil *Well-drained, organic.*
Parts used *Flowers, seeds, oil.*
Medicinal *Measles, bruises.*
Culinary *As an oil, tea.*
Precaution *Not suitable for pregnant or nursing women.*

Dried safflower blossoms hold their color well; use them to color soups, sauces, pastas, curries, and rice.

Safflower seeds are used to help lower cholesterol in the blood and prevent heart disease.

GROWING GUIDELINES

Sow seed shallowly outdoors in spring. Transplants poorly.
Growth habit Annual; height 2–3 feet (60–90 cm).
Flowers Summer; orange to yellow, thistle-like blossoms.

HARVESTING AND STORING

Collect flowers in the morning, before fully open, and use fresh. Dry for infusions.

Use safflower oil in cooking when no taste should be imparted to the food.

Infuse safflower blooms for a tea that soothes skin problems and acts as a laxative and diuretic.

Ancient caraway has been found in
the remnants of Stone-Age meals and
Egyptian tombs.

Carum carvi
CARAWAY

The seeds of this aromatic herb have been used for more than 5,000 years for flavoring food and their calmative effect. They can also be used in potpourri.

GROWING GUIDELINES

Sow seed outdoors in spring or early fall, or plant seedlings in spring to late summer. Transplants poorly.

Growth habit Biennial; height to 2 feet (60 cm).

Flowers Spring to summer; white-pink blossoms.

HARVESTING AND STORING

Snip tender leaves in spring; use fresh. After flowering, hang cut seedheads upside-down in paper bag to dry. Collect seeds and dry in sun for 2–3 days. Store in an airtight container.

Historically, caraway was thought to give protection from witches, and was also used in love potions.

Soil Fertile, light.
Parts used Leaves, roots, oil, and seeds.
Medicinal Colic, bronchitis, diarrhea, flatulence, indigestion.
Culinary Leaves in salad, soups; roots cooked as vegetables.

Seeds have a licorice taste and are used to flavor bread, cakes, cheese, and meat.

Centaurea cyanus

CORNFLOWER

This wildflower was common in cornfields throughout Europe. Its botanical name comes from the centaur Chiron, who first revealed the flower's healing powers.

To extend flowering, sow seed fortnightly from spring to summer. Add blooms to salads as a garnish.

GROWING GUIDELINES

Sow seed outdoors in spring or fall. Will self-sow.
Growth habit Hardy annual; height 8–36 inches (20–90 cm).
Flowers Spring to summer; thistle-like blooms.

HARVESTING AND STORING

Harvest flowers as they open. Use fresh or dried.

> **Soil** Well-drained.
> **Parts used** Flowers.
> **Medicinal** For minor wounds, mouth ulcers, eye inflammation.
> **Other names** Bluebottle, knapweed, bachelor's button.

Cornflower extracts are added to cosmetic and hair preparations, and dyes.

Flowers vary in color from white to bright blue, purple, pink, or red, and are a popular addition to potpourri.

Chamaemelum nobile

CHAMOMILE

Herb gardens of yesteryear often included a lush lawn of chamomile that released a sweet, apple-like scent when walked upon.

An infusion of dried chamomile flowers makes a soothing tea. Add a swirl of honey to taste.

Soil *Moist, well-drained.*
Parts used *Flowers, oil.*
Medicinal *Insomnia, stress-related illnesses, hyperactivity.*
Culinary *As a tea.*

GROWING GUIDELINES

Sow seed or divide older plants in spring. Creeping runners create a carpet-like surface.

Growth habit Perennial; height to 9 inches (22.5 cm).
Flowers Summer; small, daisy-like blooms.

HARVESTING AND STORING

Collect flowers at full bloom and dry on trays or paper. Store in tightly sealed containers.

Dried chamomile is used in both commercially prepared and homeopathic treatments.

Established chamomile lawns can be mowed like grass. In the first year, clip flowers to encourage growth.

Chrysanthemum coronarium

CHRYSANTHEMUM

Also known as florists' chrysanthemums, this attractive, easily grown herb has been valued for its medicinal qualities since the first century.

Soil Rich, well-drained.
Parts used Flowers.
Pests/diseases Aphids, slugs, snails, mildew, viruses.
Medicinal Coronary artery disease, angina, liver disorders.

GROWING GUIDELINES

Grow from root division or basal cuttings in early spring; or by seed in late winter or early spring.
Growth habit Perennial; height 1–7 feet (30–210 cm).
Flowers Late summer; single or double red, yellow, bronze, pink, or white flowers.

HARVESTING AND STORING

Harvest flowers in late fall, then dry.

Blanch flowers and add to salads; use the spicy foliage in Asian cooking.

Sunny chrysanthemums are used medicinally to treat colds and increase blood flow.

Chrysanthemum parthenium
FEVERFEW

Double-flowered feverfew makes an attractive border plant that repels undesirable insects from the garden. It is also an effective treatment for migraine.

GROWING GUIDELINES

Sow seed shallowly indoors in late winter; transplant outdoors two weeks after frosts have passed.

Growth habit Perennial; height 8–24 inches (20–60 cm).

Flowers Summer to fall; daisy-like rays with yellow centers.

HARVESTING AND STORING

Cut stems at full bloom; dry.

Soil Well-drained.
Parts used Whole plant.
Medicinal Arthritis, digestion. Herb is available in tablet form.
Precaution Not suitable for pregnant or nursing women.

Cut flowers hold their color well, making them ideal for potpourris and arrangements.

For vigorous plants, remove blossoms before seeding. Fresh leaves may cause skin allergies if eaten.

*Chicory flowers open and close
each morning and night, even
when cut for arrangements.*

Cichorium intybus
CHICORY

Look for chicory flowers along roadsides and field edges. This hardy, wild plant thrives under a variety of harsh conditions; it doesn't like the cozy warmth of indoors.

Soil *Well-drained.*
Parts used *Leaves, roots.*
Pests *Slugs, aphids.*
Medicinal *Liver complaints, gout.*
Culinary *Leaves in salads. Dried, ground roots as coffee substitute.*

GROWING GUIDELINES

Sow seed outdoors in spring. Side-dress in midsummer with compost or rotted manure. Keep moist.
Growth habit Perennial; height 3–5 feet (90–150 cm).
Flowers Early spring to fall; bright blue dandelion-like blooms.

HARVESTING AND STORING

Use leaves fresh. Collect roots in fall; dry, grind, and store in an airtight container.

Chicons, the cone-shaped heads of buds, are blanched and served as a vegetable.

167

Coriandrum sativum

CILANTRO

This annual herb, also known as coriander, has tasty, strong-smelling leaves. The seeds, which have culinary and medicinal uses, become more fragrant with age.

Cilantro is one of the world's oldest known herbs.

Soil *Fertile, well-drained.*
Parts used *Leaves, seeds, oil.*
Medicinal *Joint pain, digestive problems, hemorrhoids.*
Culinary *In Middle Eastern and Southeast Asian food.*

GROWING GUIDELINES

Sow seed deep outdoors after danger of frost, or grow indoors on a sunny windowsill. Water well.

Growth habit Annual; height to 3 feet (90 cm).

Flowers Summer; tiny, white to pink blossoms.

HARVESTING AND STORING

Harvest foliage before seeds form; use fresh. Freezes and dries poorly. Gather seeds as they ripen from midsummer.

Seeds are one of the main ingredients in curry powder, and are used to flavor stews, pastries, and wine.

A recommended companion plant, cilantro repels aphids and carrot root flies.

Crocus sativus
SAFFRON

The fragrant pink, mauve, and purple blooms of saffron with their red stigmas and long, yellow anthers are a striking and valuable addition to the garden.

GROWING GUIDELINES

Plant saffron crocus corms with rooting side down in late summer. Divide corms every 2–3 years, after spring foliage.
Growth habit Perennial; height 4–6 inches (10–15 cm).
Flowers Fall; blossoms appear before or with leaves.

HARVESTING AND STORING

Collect individual, dark yellow stigmas; dry on paper. Store in airtight glass container away from light. Dry flowers whole.

Dried "threads" of the saffron flower are used in cooking and perfumery.

Soil Well-drained, light, fertile.
Parts used Flower stigmas.
Medicinal Internally for liver problems, depression.
Culinary Flavor/color cakes, paella, risotto, bouillabaisse.

Good quality saffron is expensive because crops yield very little product: just 2 lb (1 kg) is extracted from 160,000 flowers.

Powerfully flavored seeds are roasted or crushed and added to lamb, curries, and yoghurt.

Cuminum cyminum
CUMIN

Cumin is a small and delicate member of the parsley family. The seeds have been used for centuries as a pungent addition to curries and spicy dishes.

Soil Light, well-drained.
Parts used Seeds.
Medicinal Minor digestive problems, flatulence, colic, migraine. Oil is anti-bacterial.
Culinary Seeds for flavoring.

GROWING GUIDELINES

Sow seed in spring in sheltered, sunny site. Seeds may not ripen in cool summers.
Growth habit Annual; height to 10 inches (25 cm).
Flowers Summer; white or pinkish blossoms.

HARVESTING AND STORING

Collect seeds when ripe. Use whole or grind for culinary purposes.

Midsummer blossoms produce aromatic seeds. The plant's oil is used in veterinary medicine.

The Romans used ground cumin seeds in the same way we use pepper. They also believed it stimulated sex organs.

Curcuma longa

TURMERIC

A member of the ginger family, turmeric is renowned for its musky taste and peppery fragrance. It has been used for centuries to dye the robes of Buddhist monks.

Soil *Rich, well-drained.*
Parts used *Rhizomes.*
Medicinal *Fresh or dried for liver, digestion, and circulation issues.*
Culinary *Essential ingredient in curry powder and Asian dishes.*

GROWING GUIDELINES

Propagate by root division when dormant or by sown seed in fall. Grow in a greenhouse and water well; keep dry in winter.
Growth habit Perennial; height to 3 feet (90 cm).
Flowers Late spring to midsummer; pale yellow blossoms.

HARVESTING AND STORING

Lift rhizomes during the dormant period. Boil or steam, then dry and grind.

A source of yellow-orange dye, dried turmeric root is also used as a food colorant.

Fleshy green and pink bracts sit atop 4–6 inch (10–15 cm) long spikes and surround pale yellow blossoms.

Cymbopogon citratus
LEMONGRASS

This clump-forming perennial has slim, grassy foliage and provides a contrast to broad-leaved garden herbs. Use it in cooking or as a soothing tea.

Soil *Well-drained, organic-rich.*
Parts used *Leaves, stems, oil.*
Medicinal *Digestive problems, scabies, ringworm, head lice.*
Culinary *Flavoring for food; as a tea.*

Individual leaves regularly die off; this is normal and there's no need to remove dead foliage.

GROWING GUIDELINES

Propagate by division of older plants in late spring. Trim the leaves to several inches before dividing.
Growth habit Perennial; height to 6 feet (1.8 m).
Flowers Seldom flowers.

HARVESTING AND STORING

Snip fresh foliage as needed. Harvest larger amounts in summer; dry quickly to maximize flavor.

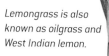

Lemongrass is also known as oilgrass and West Indian lemon.

Use the white base of leaves in Southeast Asian-style cuisine, especially with meat and fish.

Echinacea's daisy-like blossoms have a fragrant honey scent and make a superb cut flower.

Echinacea purpurea
ECHINACEA

Research has shown that echinacea stimulates the immune system, promotes rapid healing of wounds, and has anti-bacterial properties.

GROWING GUIDELINES

Propagate by seed in spring, division in spring or fall, or root cutting in late fall to early winter. Grows from thick rootstock with short rhizomes.

Growth habit Perennial; height to 4 feet (1.2 m).

Flowers Midsummer to fall; pinkish-purple blooms.

HARVESTING AND STORING

Lift plants in fall; dry roots and rhizomes.
Store in airtight containers.

Echinacea is named for the prickly scales on its flower cone. The Greek word echinos *means hedgehog.*

Soil Humus-rich, well-drained.
Parts used Roots, rhizomes.
Medicinal Coughs, colds, venereal diseases, gangrene, boils, acne, infected wounds.

Roots and rhizomes are dried and processed for use in infusions, tablets, and powders.

Elettaria cardamomum

CARDAMOM

Cardamom is one of the world's most ancient spices, and also one of the most highly valued. Only saffron and vanilla are more expensive.

Cardamom is one of the main ingredients in curry powder. Dry capsules on platforms in the sun.

Soil *Moist, humus-rich.*
Parts used *Seeds, oil.*
Medicinal *Flatulence, indigestion, stomach disorders.*
Culinary *Flavors sweetmeats, pastries, ice cream, mulled wine.*

GROWING GUIDELINES

Propagate by division of rhizomes in spring, or by seed in fall.
Growth habit Perennial; height 6–10 feet (1.8–3 m).
Flowers Spring to summer; white-and-pink spikes.

HARVESTING AND STORING

Harvest three years after planting; continue for 10–15 years. Pick fruit every few weeks before ripening; dry. Store in airtight containers.

Chew dried cardamom seeds to cleanse the breath, detoxify caffeine, and counteract mucus-forming foods.

Eye-catching cardamom flowers give way to lime-green fruit. Oil derived from the plant is used in perfume.

Equisetum spp.

HORSETAIL

A primitive, spore-bearing, grass-like plant containing silica, horsetail has often been used as a pot-scrubber and for sanding wood.

GROWING GUIDELINES

Plant in pots to contain spread. To propagate, divide mature plants in fall.

Growth habit Perennial; height 4–18 inches (10–45 cm).

Flowers Spring; spikes atop stalks.

HARVESTING AND STORING

Cut stems just above the root. Dry in sun; tie in bundles.

Horsetail is used internally to treat incontinence and conjunctivitis. Large doses, however, can be toxic.

Soil *Rich, moist.*
Parts used *Stems.*
Medicinal *Contains silica, which is used by the body in the production and repair of connective tissues and bones.*

Cone-like flowering structures release horsetail spores that are dispersed by the wind.

Almond-scented flowers are
dried for infusions; rootstock
is also aromatic when cut.

Filipendula ulmaria
MEADOWSWEET

This plant has an impressive place in history. It was from meadowsweet that the compound of salicylic acid, later known as aspirin, was isolated.

Fragrant meadowsweet flowers are used in potpourri. The plant itself produces a green dye.

GROWING GUIDELINES

Propagate by division of rootstock in fall or spring, or sow seed in early spring.

Growth habit Perennial; height to 4 feet (1.2 m).

Flowers Summer; clustered blossoms.

HARVESTING AND STORING

Harvest plant as flowering begins. Dry for use in tablets and liquid extracts.

Soil Rich, wet, low acidity.
Parts used Whole plant, flowers.
Pests/diseases Powdery mildew.
Medicinal Colds, peptic ulcers, heartburn, digestive disorders, rheumatic and joint pain.

A natural repellent, meadowsweet was used in the Middle Ages to ward off skin parasites; it was the filling for mattresses and the covering for floors.

Foeniculum vulgare

FENNEL

Grow licorice-scented fennel as a tall ornamental in the garden and for its culinary uses. The leaves and seeds are also used in cosmetics and herbal medicines.

To promote leaf growth, remove seedheads. To preserve leaf flavor, add at the end of the recipe.

GROWING GUIDELINES

Sow seed shallowly outdoors in spring or fall. Keep moist.

Growth habit Perennial; height to 4 feet (1.2 m).

Flowers Summer; small, aromatic, yellow blossoms.

HARVESTING AND STORING

Snip leaves before blooming. Use fresh or freeze. Cut ripe seed heads, place in paper bag, and shake. Dry on paper.

Soil Humusy, well-drained.
Parts used Whole plant.
Medicinal Indigestion, colic, sore throat, gum disease, lactation.
Culinary With fish; in salads; as vegetable.

Every part of the fennel plant, including the onion-like bulb is edible.

Nectar-rich fennel flowers attract beneficials, such as pollinating wasps, to the garden.

Ginkgo biloba

GINKGO

An ancient species of plant that is often referred to as a "living fossil", ginkgo contains a chemical that is important in blocking allergic responses.

Soil Deep, moist, humus-rich.
Parts used Leaves, seeds.
Medicinal Allergic inflammation, asthma, blood circulation.
Culinary Nuts are roasted.
Precaution May cause vomiting.

The fan-shaped leaves measure up to 5 inches (12 cm) across and turn yellow in the fall.

GROWING GUIDELINES

Plants are male or female. Take cuttings of male in summer; females bear evil-smelling fruit. Sow ripe seeds in fall.
Growth habit Deciduous; height to 120 feet (36 m).
Flowers Spring; inconspicuous green blooms on females.

HARVESTING AND STORING

Pick leaves in fall as they change color; dry. Cook seed kernels. Store both in airtight containers.

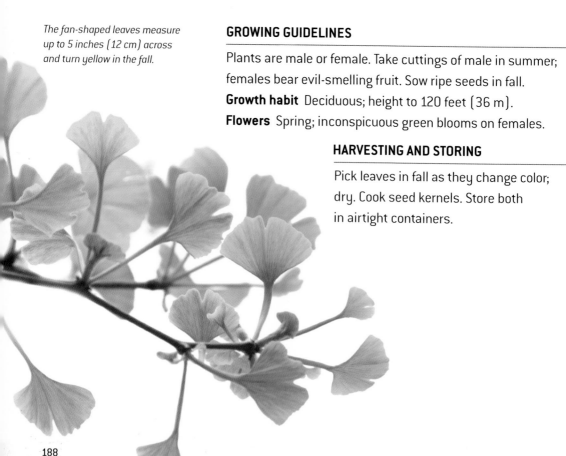

The pyramid-shaped ginkgo is also known as a maidenhair tree. Nurture young plants with organic mulch.

The roots are boiled to extract the familiar black substance that is used in licorice candy and as a foaming agent in beer.

Glycyrrhiza glabra
LICORICE

The bittersweet licorice root has been enjoyed as a natural confection for thousands of years. The legumous plant is native to southwestern Asia and the Mediterranean.

> **Soil** *Deep, rich, moist.*
> **Parts used** *Roots, stolons.*
> **Medicinal** *Constipation, asthma, bronchitis, coughs, shingles.*
> **Precaution** *For use by qualified practitioners only.*

GROWING GUIDELINES

Divide rootstock, take stolon cuttings, or grow from seed in spring or fall. Remove flowerheads for stronger roots.
Growth habit Perennial; height 2–5 feet (60–150 cm).
Flowers Summer; pale blue or purple blossoms.

HARVESTING AND STORING

Lift roots and stolons in early fall 3–4 years after planting. Dry for decoctions, liquid extracts, lozenges, and powder.

Licorice is used to flavor sweets, ice cream, beverages, and pharmaceutical products.

Hamamelis virginiana

WITCH HAZEL

Hardy witch hazel has wild, scented flowers and its forked branches are used as water-divining rods. An extract from its bark has been a popular astringent for centuries.

Soil Moist, humus-rich.
Parts used Leaves, branches, bark, and twigs.
Medicinal Dysentery, diarrhea, burns, sore throats, eye and skin inflammations.

GROWING GUIDELINES

Propagate by seed planted outdoors in fall, or take cuttings or layers from established plants in spring.
Growth habit Deciduous shrub; height 8–15 feet (2.4–4.5 m).
Flowers Fall; thread-like petals.

HARVESTING AND STORING

Collect leaves in summer; branches, twigs, and bark in spring.

An infusion of flower-bearing twigs can be used on a compress to treat bruises, sprains, and insect bites.

Effervescent witch hazel flowers produce black seed capsules that can take two years to germinate.

Helianthus annuus

SUNFLOWER

All parts of the sunflower are usable. Each flower contains more than 1,000 seeds. The plant has been used medicinally for more than 3,000 years.

GROWING GUIDELINES

Sow seed in spring. Support stems with stakes.

Water regularly for larger seedheads.

Growth habit Annual; height 3–10 feet (90–300 cm).

Flowers Summer; yellow-petalled blossoms.

HARVESTING AND STORING

Cut whole plant as flowering begins. Collect seeds in fall.

Rub seedheads to dislodge seeds. Store in airtight containers.

Soil Rich, well-drained.
Parts used Whole plant, oil.
Medicinal Malaria, bronchial infections, tuberculosis.
Culinary Oil in cooking; fresh or roasted seeds in cereal, bread.

Sunflower seeds make a morish snack. They are also pressed for oil.

The sunflower has always been revered as an emblem of the sun. It also attracts beneficial insects.

Hypericum perforatum

ST JOHN'S WORT

When crushed or soaked in oil, St John's wort flowers exude a bright red pigment similar to blood. The plant has been valued as a talisman against evil for centuries.

Dried St John's wort is used in liquid extracts and medicated oils, as well as traditionally in anointing oil.

GROWING GUIDELINES

Propagate by cuttings after flowering, by seed in spring, or division in fall. Prune stems in early spring.

Growth habit Perennial; height 10–36 inches (25–90 cm).

Flowers Summer and early fall; five-petalled, yellow blooms.

Soil Well-drained to dry.
Parts used Whole plant, oil.
Medicinal Depression, premenstrual tension, shingles, sciatica, wounds, bruising, burns.
Precaution Only use under professional supervision.

HARVESTING AND STORING

Harvest plants as flowering begins.
Use fresh or dried.

St John's wort berries are harmful if eaten. Plant their small, dark brown seeds 2 feet (60 cm) apart in spring.

Sunny St John's wort flowers are a source of red dye. The plant is also used in cosmetics and, most recently, in AIDS drug trials.

Hyssop is noted in the Old Testament as being used for purification. The delicate blossoms attract honeybees.

Hyssopus officinalis

HYSSOP

The flowers of this evergreen shrub attract beneficial insects. An excellent border plant in knot gardens, hyssop produces an oil that's used in liqueurs.

Soil *Light, well-drained.*
Parts used *Whole plant.*
Medicinal *Colds, flu, bronchitis, flatulence, cuts, burns, bruises.*
Precaution *Essential oil may cause convulsions. Use diluted.*

GROWING GUIDELINES

Take cuttings or divide mature plants in spring or fall. Prune in spring; lightly mulch.
Growth habit Perennial; height 1–2 feet (30–60 cm).
Flowers Summer; spikes of blue-violet blooms.

HARVESTING AND STORING

For medicinal use, harvest only green material. Cut stems just before flowers open and hang to dry. Store in airtight containers.

Leaves have a sage-mint flavor; use sparingly with meat and legumes.

Iris 'Florentina'

ORRIS

The dried root of orris is used as a fixative in perfumery and potpourri, and has a strong violet fragrance. It is also used in breath fresheners and dental products.

Soil *Deep, rich, well-drained.*
Parts used *Rhizomes.*
Medicinal *Coughs, excess mucus, diarrhea, deep cuts.*
Precaution *All iris species are harmful if eaten.*

GROWING GUIDELINES

Plant after flowering, leaving the tip of the rhizome above the soil.
Growth habit Perennial; height to 30 inches (75 cm).
Flowers Spring to summer; white blossoms with yellow beards.

HARVESTING AND STORING

Harvest at maturity. For root aroma, lift in fall. Wash, split, cut into small pieces, then dry. Grind to powder and store in dark glass container for at least two years; the violet fragrance needs time to mature.

Divide orris roots every 2–3 years in early fall to promote flowering.

With its striking bearded blooms and fanlike spray of leaves, orris is an attractive garden addition.

Both male and female plants are required for fruiting. Green at first, berries ripen to a bruised blue.

Juniperus communis
COMMON JUNIPER

Juniper is an evergreen, coniferous shrub that has been used for centuries for its medicinal properties. It is a bitter, aromatic herb with antiseptic properties.

> **Soil** *Tolerant of most conditions.*
> **Parts used** *Berries, oil.*
> **Medicinal** *Digestion, kidney inflammation, rheumatism.*
> **Precautions** *Not suitable for pregnant women.*

GROWING GUIDELINES

Sow seed in pots in fall. Grow seedlings in nursery rows outdoors for 1–2 years before permanent planting.
Growth habit Shrub; height to 20 feet (6 m).
Flowers Spring; yellow or green blossoms.

HARVESTING AND STORING

Shake branches to harvest berries; use fresh for oil distillation, or dry.

Berries are added to game dishes, pickles, and pork. Oil distilled from the fruit is used to flavor gin.

Laurus nobilis
SWEET BAY

Bay is the only laurel that is not poisonous. Bay leaf garlands represent victory. Use leaves for flavor in soups and stews, or add to potpourri.

Soil *Rich, well-drained.*
Parts used *Leaves.*
Medicinal *Indigestion, flatulence, sprains, colic, rheutmatism.*
Culinary *In sauces, soups, stews.*
Other names *Bay or true laurel.*

GROWING GUIDELINES

Take fresh green cuttings in fall. Keep soil moist; germination may take 3–9 months. Sow seed outdoors in warm climates; germination may take 6–12 months.
Growth habit Evergreen tree; height to 50 feet (15 m).
Flowers Spring; yellowish blooms.

HARVESTING AND STORING

Use leaves fresh or dried.
Store in airtight containers.

This evergreen tree grows well in pots and is easily trained as a standard.

*Leathery leaves hold their flavor well.
Add whole at the beginning of a
recipe; remove before serving.*

*Sweet bay produces inedible
berries. Dried leaves are used in
kitchen cupboards to repel pests.*

Lavandula angustifolia

ENGLISH LAVENDER

Most gardeners and herb growers never have enough lavender. The silvery foliage and purple blossoms are stunning in borders, and the flowers attract bees.

GROWING GUIDELINES

Take cuttings from side shoots in summer. Place in well-drained compost; transplant as soon as they root. Remove first flowers to encourage growth. Prune after flowering; don't cut old wood—it won't regrow.

Growth habit Shrub; height to 3 feet (90 cm).

Flowers Summer; lavender-blue blossoms.

Soil *Light, well-drained.*
Parts used *Flowers, oil.*
Medicinal *Depression, anxiety, indigestion, migraines, cold sores, halitosis, bronchitis.*
Culinary *In jams, ice cream, vinegar, scones; as garnish.*

Lavender bushes are known to repel flies and ticks; plant en masse near outdoor entertaining areas.

Lavender oil is distilled from glands tucked around the tiny hairs on the flowers, leaves, and stems.

HARVESTING AND STORING

For scent, gather flowers on opening in dry weather. Hang bunches upside-down, away from light, to dry.

SPECIAL TIPS

Plant lavender as a hedge or in knot gardens. In borders, combine lavender with other plants that need excellent drainage, such as yarrow and rosemary. Incorporate into vegetable gardens to attract beneficial insects.

Relaxing lavender oil is used in soaps, perfumes, and cleaning products, as well as added to baths. It is also applied topically to rejuvenate skin on the face and hands.

French lavender is an antiseptic herb with a rosemary-like scent and dark purple flowers. It is less hardy than the English variety.

A recommended companion plant for tomatoes, lovage does well in pots. Its leaves, stems, and stalks have a savory, celery-like flavor.

Levisticum officinale

LOVAGE

Some companion gardeners claim that lovage improves the growth and flavor of vegetable crops. If you can't grow celery, try this easy substitute.

Blanch young shoots and eat as a vegetable. The stalks can be candied.

GROWING GUIDELINES

Sow seed shallowly in early fall. Prune flowers to encourage growth. Mulch in spring with compost or manure.

Growth habit Perennial; height to 6 feet (1.8 m).

Flowers Summer; green-yellow blossoms.

HARVESTING AND STORING

Harvest leaves as required. Bunch foliage and stems in fall; hang to dry, or blanch and freeze. Collect seeds when fruit splits. Lift roots in fall; wash, slice, and dry.

Soil Fertile, moist, well-drained.
Parts used Leaves, stems, roots, seeds, oil.
Medicinal Indigestion, flatulence, kidney stones, colic, sore throats.
Culinary Use as you would celery.

Add fresh or dried chopped leaves to potato salads, cream-based soups, and savory dishes.

Melissa officinalis
LEMON BALM

This ornamental and aromatic herb has been cultivated for more than 2,000 years. The strongly scented leaves are said to soothe coughs when taken as a syrup.

Soil *Well-drained.*
Parts used *Whole plant, oil.*
Medicinal *Indigestion, insect bites, depression, headaches, herpes, feverish colds, gout.*
Other names *Sweet balm.*

GROWING GUIDELINES

Sow shallowly in spring. Take cuttings or divide older plants in spring or fall. Prune old stalks in fall.
Growth habit Perennial; height 1–2 feet (30–60 cm).
Flowers Summer; white, tubular blossoms.

HARVESTING AND STORING

Collect leaves in late summer. Use fresh, or dry quickly. Cut entire plant, leaving 2 inches (5 cm) of stem.

Grow lemon balm in pots and move it around the garden to attract beneficial honeybees.

Add fresh leaves to summer salads, soup, herb vinegar, and fish, or infuse dried leaves to make a calming tea.

Chew fresh leaves to relieve bad breath; add to iced water or tea for a refreshing summer drink.

Mentha spp.
MINT

Mints are herbaceous perennials that thrive in most locations. Both fresh and dried foliage provide flavor to sweet and savory dishes.

GROWING GUIDELINES

Propagate from new plants that spring up along roots, or by cuttings in spring or fall. Mow large areas frequently (as you would a lawn).
Growth habit Perennial; height to 30 inches (75 cm).
Flowers Summer; tiny purple or pink blossoms.

HARVESTING AND STORING

Pick leaves as required. Just before blooming, cut stalks and hang in bunches to dry. Store in airtight containers.

One of the many varieties of the mint genus, M. x piperita 'Chocolate' emits a delicious choc-mint scent.

Soil Rich, moist, well-drained.
Parts used Whole plant, oil.
Medicinal Skin irritations, minor burns, ringworm, sinusitis.
Culinary Meat, salad, fruit, tea.

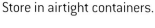
Mints are rampant spreaders. To control, plant in large pots. Water well to maximize flavor.

215

PEPPERMINT

Peppermint has a long medicinal history; archeological evidence proves it has been used for at least the last 10,000 years. It remains popular today.

Soil *Moist, well-drained.*
Parts used *Whole plant, oil.*
Medicinal *Colds, insomnia, headaches, abdominal pains.*
Culinary *As a tea; flavoring for ice cream, confectionary.*

GROWING GUIDELINES

Propagate by cuttings or division in spring or fall.
Requires lots of water. Rarely produces seed.
Growth habit Perennial; height 2–4 feet (60–120 cm).
Flowers Summer; purple blooms form thick spikes.

HARVESTING AND STORING

Harvest leaves as required. Use fresh, freeze, or infuse in oil or vinegar. Store dried leaves in airtight containers.

Indigenous to Europe, peppermint is now cultivated worldwide.

Peppermint tea is said to have a calming effect on digestive disorders. Leaves and oil are also used to flavor toothpaste.

Monarda didyma

BEE BALM (BERGAMOT)

This North American native has a citrusy fragrance and wildly colorful blossoms that attract beneficial insects and nectar-eating birds to the garden.

Plant bee balm, also known as Oswego tea, near tomatoes and peppers to enhance their growth.

GROWING GUIDELINES

Grow from seed, cutting, or division in spring. For fall blooms, prune stems after first flowering.

Growth habit Perennial; height 3–4 feet (90–120 cm).

Flowers Summer; red to pink and lavender to white blossoms.

HARVESTING AND STORING

Harvest leaves for tea just before flowering; dry quickly for best flavor. Pull individual blooms for a colorful garnish.

Soil Rich, moist, light.
Parts used Whole plant.
Medicinal Digestive problems, colds, headaches, sore throats.
Culinary Leaves in salads and stuffing; as a tea, in iced drinks.

Bee balm tea became popular in New England after the Boston Tea Party of 1773.

Flowers can be eaten fresh, added to salads as a garnish, or used in arrangements and potpourris.

Summer flowering sweet cicely produces chocolate-colored fruits and licorice-flavored seeds.

Myrrhis odorata

SWEET CICELY

Sweet cicely, an ornamental and frost-hardy herb, is also known as sweet chervil, anise, or myrrh. It has a scent like lovage and a licorice taste.

> **Soil** *Rich, moist, well-drained.*
> **Parts used** *Leaves, roots, seeds.*
> **Medicinal** *Minor digestive problems, anemia.*
> **Culinary** *Leaves and seeds in salads; roots as vegetable.*

GROWING GUIDELINES

Sow seed shallowly outdoors, or divide older plants, in fall or spring. Mulch with well-rotted compost or manure.
Growth habit Perennial; height to 3 feet (90 cm).
Flowers Summer; white blossoms.

HARVESTING AND STORING

Collect leaves as required in summer. Dry seedheads on paper in shade. Harvest roots after first year. Scrub and use fresh like parsnips, or dry.

Delicate cicely leaves are used as a low-calorie sweetener for desserts.

221

Nasturtium officinale
WATERCRESS

A herb whose ideal habitat is shallow, free-flowing water, watercress abounds with vitamins and minerals, is a valuable medicinal plant, and has a peppery taste.

Soil *Slightly alkaline water.*
Parts used *Leaves.*
Medicinal *Skin disorders, spring tonic, bronchitis, rheumatism.*
Culinary *Leaves in salads, soups; as a juice.*

GROWING GUIDELINES

Propagate by root cuttings in water. Can be grown in pots in a rich potting compost; stand pots in water changed daily.
Growth habit Aquatic perennial.
Flowers Summer; small white blooms.

HARVESTING AND STORING

Cut leaves as required; use fresh.

Don't harvest from the wild; pollutants and bacteria may be present in watercourses.

Grow watercress in full sun in water 50°F (10°C) or warmer. Harvest and juice leaves for use as a zesty spring tonic.

Nepeta cataria

CATMINT

Closely related to mint and similarly handy, catmint grows wild among weeds in gardens and fields. Cats find its scent irresistible and will roll playfully in its leaves.

Soil *Dry, sandy.*
Parts used *Whole plant.*
Medicinal *Insomnia, colds, influenza, palpitations, colic. Tea used to calm nerves.*
Other names *Catnip.*

GROWING GUIDELINES

Sow seed outdoors in spring. Take softwood cuttings in spring or summer. Transplants poorly.
Growth habit Perennial; height 1–3 feet (30–60 cm).
Flowers Summer to fall; blue-violet blossoms.

HARVESTING AND STORING

Strip topmost leaves in summer. Use fresh, or dry on trays in shade. Store in tightly sealed jars.

Leaves and flowering tops contain vitamin C; add to salads, sauces, and stews.

Infuse dried leaves for a calmative, mint-flavored tea, or use to stuff cat toys.

Grow catmint in pots to contain its aggressive spread, or plant near eggplant (aubergine) and turnips to reduce flea beetle infestations.

Plant near peppers and tomatoes to enhance their growth, or grow in pots on a sunny windowsill for easy picking.

Ocimum basilicum

SWEET BASIL

Sweet basil is one of the most popular herbs in home gardens because of its strong flavor (with hints of licorice and pepper), which is so useful in the kitchen.

Use dried basil leaf to make a tea to aid digestion; add about 1 teaspoon to 1 cup (250 ml) of boiling water.

GROWING GUIDELINES

Sow seed indoors in seed trays in mid-spring. Transplant seedlings to pots; move outside to warm, sheltered spot.

Growth habit Perennial; height to 2 feet (60 cm).

Flowers Midsummer; white blossoms.

HARVESTING AND STORING

Harvest leaves weekly; chop and freeze for best flavor.

Soil Rich, well-drained.
Parts used Whole plant, oil.
Medicinal Colds, acne, nausea, migraine, insomnia, insect stings.
Culinary Leaves in salads, pasta sauces, soups, meat dishes.

To make pesto, mix fresh leaves, olive oil, parmesan cheese, garlic, and nuts. If freezing, add garlic just before use.

227

Ocimum basilicum 'Horapha'

THAI BASIL

Tropical Thai basil has purple-flushed, lance-like leaves that have a sweet licorice scent. Water well before harvesting to maximize flavor.

Soil *Rich, well-drained.*
Parts used *Leaves, stems, oil.*
Medicinal *Insect bites, anxiety, migraines, depression.*
Culinary *As condiment in Thai and Vietnamese cooking.*

If growing basil to eat, remove its small, delicate flowers before blossoming—they usurp taste.

GROWING GUIDELINES

Sow seed indoors in mid-spring. Transplant seedlings to pots and move outside to a warm, sheltered spot.
Growth habit Perennial; height to 18 inches (45 cm).
Flowers Mid to late summer; mauve-pink blossoms.

HARVESTING AND STORING

Harvest in the early morning for maximum flavor. Remove leaves from stem tops; use fresh or freeze immediately.

Thai basil is a colorful herb garden addition. Its leaves have a more assertive taste than other varieties.

Crimson-colored buds bloom from mid to late summer. A leaf in your pocket is believed to attract money and guard against negativity.

Oenothera biennis

EVENING PRIMROSE

Oil from the evening primrose plant contains chemicals that assist the body to regulate hormone systems, especially in women.

Soil Dry, sandy.
Parts used Oil, seeds, roots.
Medicinal Premenstrual and menopausal conditions, acne, skin problems, asthma.
Culinary All parts are edible.

GROWING GUIDELINES

Propagate by seed in spring and fall.
Self-sows regularly.
Growth habit Biennial; height 5 feet (1.5 m).
Flowers Summer; bright yellow blossoms.

HARVESTING AND STORING

Collect seeds when ripe and process for oil.
Harvest roots in second year; use fresh.

The evening primrose plant produces downy capsules filled with tiny seeds. Beneficial oil distilled from the seeds is used in cosmetic preparations.

Evening primrose flowers emit phosphorescent light and a thick, sweet scent at night.

Origanum majorana

SWEET MARJORAM

Sweet marjoram is a bushy, aromatic herb with lush foliage and a mild oregano taste. Its flowers attract beneficial insects to the garden.

GROWING GUIDELINES

Sow shallowly indoors in spring. Transplant outside after frosts have passed. Divide in fall.

Growth habit Perennial; height to 2 feet (60 cm).

Flowers Summer; white or pink blossoms.

HARVESTING AND STORING

Cut fresh leaves as needed. Hang in bunches to dry. Store in airtight containers.

Soil Light, well-drained.
Parts used Whole plant, oil.
Medicinal Insomnia, sprains, headaches, bronchitis, arthritis.
Precaution Not suitable for pregnant women.

Use dried with meat, cheese, and beans—particularly in Italian and Greek dishes.

Add fresh marjoram leaves to vinegar for long-lasting flavor. Oil is distilled for use in liqueurs, perfumes, and soap.

Origanum vulgare
OREGANO

The sprigs of oregano, with their small, rounded leaves and miniature blossoms, make an attractive garnish. Use it as a border plant or in flower beds.

Most often used dried, flavorsome oregano is important in Mexican, Spanish, Greek, and Italian cooking.

GROWING GUIDELINES

Sow outdoors after frost has passed. Take cuttings or divide roots in spring or early fall.

Growth habit Perennial; 12–30 inches (30–75 cm).
Flowers Summer; rose-purple blossoms.

HARVESTING AND STORING

Snip fresh sprigs as required in summer. Hang foliage in bunches to dry. Store in airtight containers.

Soil Well-drained.
Parts used Whole plant, oil.
Medicinal Colds, stomach upsets, bronchitis, asthma.
Precaution Not suitable for pregnant women.

Use cuttings to propagate oregano; seedlings don't always retain the flavor of the original plant.

Like other strongly aromatic herbs, oregano has gained a reputation as an effective pest repellent.

Ginseng was used during the Vietnam War to treat gunshot wounds. It contains properties that have been patented for use in anti-tumor drugs.

Panax ginseng
GINSENG

Ginseng is the most famous of all Chinese medicines. It is credited with the magical properties of long life, strength, and happiness.

Dried ginseng root has been used for centuries as a cure-all and an aphrodisiac, and for relaxation.

GROWING GUIDELINES

Propagate by seed in spring. Germination is slow.
Growth habit Perennial: height 28–36 inches (70–90 cm).
Flowers Spring and summer; greenish-white blossoms.

HARVESTING AND STORING

Lift roots from plants five years or older; use fresh or dried in powders and pills. Use fresh flowers for tonics.

Soil Moist, well-drained.
Parts used Roots, flowers.
Medicinal Insomnia, stress, nerves; to increase stamina.
Precaution May cause raised blood pressure, headaches.

Rarely found in the wild today, ginseng has carrot-shaped, aromatic rootstock.

Passiflora incarnata

PASSIONFLOWER

Missionaries regarded the flowers of this plant as symbols of Christ's passion. It is a climbing species with edible fruit, which is used medicinally.

GROWING GUIDELINES

Propagate by seed in spring or semi-ripe cuttings in summer. Mulch in spring. Prune old growth in winter.

Growth habit Perennial; height 25–30 feet (7.5–9 m).

Flowers Early to late summer; sweet-scented, white or lavender blossoms.

HARVESTING AND STORING

Collect fruit in summer when ripe. Use fresh, or freeze pulp in ice cube trays.

Soil Fertile, well-drained.
Parts used Whole plant, fruit.
Medicinal Insomnia, headaches, asthma, shingles. Use only under professional supervision.
Culinary Pulp in jams, juices.

Ripe passionflower fruit ranges in color from yellow to orange, and contains a sweet, seeded pulp.

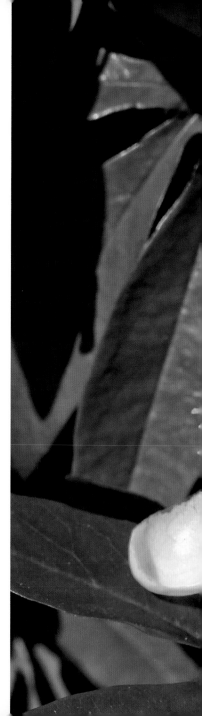

Well-watered plants produce
ornamental blossoms, then fruit.
Crushed leaves soothe minor cuts.

Petroselinum crispum

PARSLEY

Parsley is required in so many recipes, to flavor savory dishes or as a garnish, that it is a feature of most herb gardens. Grow in beds or on a sunny windowsill.

GROWING GUIDELINES

Sow seed shallowly in batches from early spring; germinates slowly. Top-dress wth rotted compost mid season.

Growth habit Biennial; height 1 foot (30 cm).

Flowers Spring of second year; greenish-yellow umbels.

HARVESTING AND STORING

Cut leaf stalks at base for fresh foliage all summer. Hang in bunches to dry, or freeze whole or chopped. Lift roots in late fall; dry. Collect seeds when ripe.

Dried parsley loses its flavor quickly. To combat this, chop and then freeze fresh leaf in zippered plastic bags.

Soil Rich; well-drained.
Parts used Whole plant.
Medicinal Cystitis, anemia, anorexia, arthritis, indigestion.
Precaution Not suitable for pregnant women or people with kidney damage.

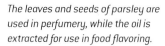

The leaves and seeds of parsley are used in perfumery, while the oil is extracted for use in food flavoring.

Interplanted parsley may help invigorate tomatoes, and repel asparagus- and rose-eating bugs.

Feed with a nitrogen-based fertilizer, but not too close to the plant's base; it may burn the roots.

Petroselinum crispum 'Italian'

ITALIAN PARSLEY

The dark green foliage of Italian or flat-leaved parsley has a stronger flavor than the curly-leaved variety. It is also larger and hardier.

Soil *Consistently moist.*
Parts used *Leaves.*
Medicinal *Kidney and bladder infections, menstrual pain.*
Culinary *Leaves in soups, stews, salads, tea, fish and meat dishes.*

GROWING GUIDELINES

Sow seeds in early spring after frosts have passed. Fertilize seedlings with nitrogen to promote growth.

Growth habit Biennial; height to 1 foot (30 cm).

Flowers Summer; small, white blossoms.

HARVESTING AND STORING

Collect outer leaves throughout summer. Use fresh, or dry and store in airtight containers for up to six months.

Italian parsley complements tomato-based dishes, and has been used for centuries to freshen breath.

Pimpinella anisum

ANISE

Use these licorice-scented leaves and spicy seeds in salads, especially when combined with apples. The seeds enhance the fragrance of potpourris.

Soil *Light, well-drained.*
Parts used *Leaves, seeds, oil.*
Medicinal *Coughs, bronchitis, indigestion, flatulence, lice.*
Culinary *Leaves in salads; oil to flavor drinks.*

GROWING GUIDELINES

Sow seed outdoors in spring. Transplants poorly. Self-sows.
Growth habit Annual: height to 2 feet (60 cm).
Flowers Summer; dainty, white blossoms.

HARVESTING AND STORING

Clip off seed head into a bag when seeds detach easily. Shake to remove seeds, then dry on paper for several days outdoors. Store in airtight containers.
Snip foliage as required.

Seeds produce a licoricey flavor that's used in confectionary.

Anise produces lacy umbels of summer flowers that attract insects. It is often used as a companion plant.

Piper nigrum
PEPPER

Undoubtedly one of the most familiar and indispensable of cooking herbs, black pepper was once so highly valued it was traded ounce for ounce with gold.

Ground or whole black peppercorns have been used for centuries to add flavor to food.

GROWING GUIDELINES

Propagate by semi-ripe cuttings in summer or by seed when available. Keep well fed and watered. Cut back young plants to stimulate growth.
Growth habit Climber; height to 12 feet (4 m).
Flowers Spring; small, white blossoms.

HARVESTING AND STORING

Collect berries in spring and summer. For black peppercorns, dry unripe berries. For white, ferment ripe, red berries. Tree-ripened red corns are rare.

Soil Rich, moist; compost.
Parts used Fruits.
Medicinal Aids digestion, nasal decongestion.
Fact Pepper accounts for one-quarter of the world spice trade.

Whole peppercorns—black, white, and red—retain their flavor well. Store in airtight jars.

Harvest fresh, unripe berries and pickle or freeze-dry to produce green peppercorns.

Spiked flowerheads range from 2–10 inches (5–25 cm) in length and attract beneficial insects.

Plantago major
PLANTAIN

Plantain is a common garden weed but was once believed to be an indispensable cure-all. Try young leaves in salads, or add to dishes that call for spinach.

Often called the Bandaid plant, plantain is used to relieve stings and bites.

GROWING GUIDELINES

Sow seed shallowly outdoors in early spring or fall.
Growth habit Perennial; height 6–8 inches (15–45 cm).
Flowers Summer; purplish-green to yellow blossoms.

HARVESTING AND STORING

Lift roots in fall, scrub well, and dry until brittle. Store in airtight containers. Pull leaves at any time; use fresh, dried, or infused in oil.

Soil *Well-drained, moist.*
Parts used *Leaves, roots.*
Medicinal *Cystitis, bronchitis, asthma, hayfever, bee stings.*
Culinary *Leaves in salads, as vegetable.*

Soothing plaintain tea treats diarrhea, yeast infections, and chesty coughs.

Rosa canina

DOG ROSE

The fragrant flowers and aromatic fruits have medicinal properties and are used for making perfume. The plant is high in antioxidants.

Dog roses were cultivated in the wild during times of scarcity, such as war, for their healing properties.

GROWING GUIDELINES

Propagate from seed or by hardwood cuttings in fall, or by budding in summer. Mulch in spring; prune in winter to maintain shape.

Growth habit Perennial; height to 10 feet (3 m).
Flowers Summer; deep pink to white.

HARVESTING AND STORING

Gather petals when flowers are opening; distill for oil and rosewater, or dry quickly on screens or paper. Collect rosehips in fall when ripe. Dry, or use to make vinegar, preserves, and wine.

Soil *Well-drained, moist.*
Parts used *Petals, fruits.*
Medicinal *Diarrhea, sore throats, eye irritations.*
Culinary *Fruit as a tea; petals added to salads or crystallized.*

Berry-like rosehips (fruits) are rich in vitamin C. Soothing rosehip tea treats colds and scurvy.

Rosa canina *was named after its
use in the 18th and 19th centuries,
to treat the bite of a rabid dog.*

Rosmarinus officinalis

ROSEMARY

The flowers and leaves of this highly scented herb are used to season and garnish meat, poultry, and fish. Rosemary is also used as an insect repellent.

Soil *Light, well-drained.*
Parts used *Leaves, flowers, oil.*
Medicinal *Headaches, arthritis, depression, nervous tension, poor circulation, dandruff.*
Culinary *As flavoring.*

GROWING GUIDELINES

Sow seed shallowly indoors in spring, then transplant to pots outdoors, or take cutting from new growth in fall, or layer young shoots in summer. Keep warm in winter.
Prune after flowering for bushy growth.
Growth habit Shrub; height 2–6 feet (60–180 cm).
Flowers Spring and summer; pale blue to lilac blossoms.

HARVESTING AND STORING

Collect leaves and flowering tops in spring and early summer. Distill for oil, or dry for extracts, spirits, and infusions. Snip fresh foliage as required.

Rosemary is a symbol of friendship and is traditionally worn at funerals and remembrance services.

Delicate rosemary blooms attract beneficial bees, and are added to soups, stews, and oil as a garnish.

Rubus idaeus

RASPBERRY

Summer- and fall-fruiting varieties of this popular crop can be grown. Raspberries have captured the essence of summer for centuries.

Clusters of pollen-rich flowers attract honeybees to the garden before transforming into conical fruits.

GROWING GUIDELINES

Propagate by division or layering of healthy stock.

Remove old stems after fruiting.

Growth habit Deciduous shrub.

Flowers Summer; small, white blossoms.

HARVESTING AND STORING

Pick leaves just before flowering; use fresh in tea.

Harvest berries when ripe.

Soil Fertile, well-drained.
Parts used Leaves, fruits.
Medicinal Digestive disorders; mouth, eye, and gum infections.
Culinary Eat fruit fresh, make into cordials, syrups, wines, vinegars.

Raspberry leaf tea is given as a childbirth preparation; don't use in early pregnancy.

Rich in vitamin C, raspberries ripen at different rates, providing juicy, plump fruit all summer long.

Rumex acetosa

SORREL

When growing in meadows, the summer stalks of sorrel's reddish-green flowers make the entire area appear to be tinted red.

GROWING GUIDELINES

Sow seed shallowly outdoors in late spring, or divide older plants in early spring or fall.
Growth habit Perennial; height to 24 inches (60 cm).
Flowers Midsummer; greenish to red blooms.

HARVESTING AND STORING

Collect outer leaves regularly to promote new growth. Eat leaves fresh, or blanch and freeze.

Soil *Fertile, moist.*
Parts used *Leaves.*
Culinary *Fresh leaves in salads, soups, cream cheese, egg dishes.*
Precaution *Not for people with rheumatism, arthritis, gout.*

Juice from the leaves is used to remove mold, and grass and ink stains from linen and wood.

Sorrel produces a whorled, reddish flower and is a good companion to garlic, chives, oregano, and sage.

Use sage as a border plant; it reaches an appreciable size in just one season.

Salvia officinalis
SAGE

An easy-to-grow herb, sage has aromatic foliage and is used fresh and dried in cooking and herbal medicines. Its velvety texture adds a soft accent to the garden.

Antioxidant-rich sage leaves are infused for use as a nerve and blood tonic, and to help reduce sweating.

GROWING GUIDELINES

Sow seed shallowly outdoors in late spring. Trim back drastically the following spring to promote vigorous growth. Repeat annually.
Growth habit Perennial; height 1–2 feet (30–60 cm).
Flowers Spring; purple blossoms.

HARVESTING AND STORING

Snip fresh leaves as required, or bunch and hang to dry for winter use.
Don't harvest in first year.

Soil Well-drained.
Parts used Leaves, oil, flowers.
Medicinal Indigestion, flatulence, depression, insect bites.
Culinary Leaves flavor meat, oil, vinegar, cheese, butter; as a tea.
Precaution Not for pregnant women or epileptics.

Sage flowers attract bees and other beneficial insects. Once spent, flowers should be removed to promote growth.

Salvia sclarea

CLARY

Fresh clary has a bitter, warm aroma and flavor, and makes an enticing flowering garden plant. It has the same culinary uses as sage.

> *Soil* Average, well-drained.
> *Parts used* Leaves, flowers, seeds, oil.
> *Medicinal* Ulcers, vomiting, cuts.
> *Precaution* Not for pregnant women. May cause drowsiness.

GROWING GUIDELINES

Sow seed outdoors in spring, or propagate by division of two-year-old plants in spring.
Growth habit Biennial; height to 5 feet (1.5 m).
Flowers Spring and summer; cream and lilac to blue blossoms.

HARVESTING AND STORING

Snip leaves for fresh use. Strip leaves and dry on trays for potpourri.

Clary tea is an effective treatment for nausea. Cooled, it is used as an eyewash to remove foreign bodies.

Oil distilled from the flowering stems is used in massage and as a fixative in perfumes.

Sambucus nigra

ELDER

Elder has been highly valued for centuries and has been termed "the medicine chest of the people" due to its many medicinal properties.

Soil *Moist, rich.*
Parts used *Leaves, bark, flowers, and fruit.*
Medicinal *Colds, fevers, arthritis, constipation, minor burns.*
Culinary *Flavor fruit, jellies, jams.*

GROWING GUIDELINES

Propagate by softwood cuttings in summer or by sown seed in fall. Prune back hard in winter.
Growth habit Deciduous shrub/tree; height to 30 feet (9 m).
Flowers Summer; scented, white blossoms.

HARVESTING AND STORING

Pick leaves in spring and summer; use fresh. Strip bark in winter and dry. Pick flowers when fully open and dry. Collect fruit when ripe; use fresh or dried.

Sweetly scented elder flowers are used in cosmetics, skin lotions, ointments, and oils.

Elder berries are used to make a sauce for duck and venison. They are harmful, however, if eaten raw.

Santolina blossoms are striking en masse, or when dried and added to potpourri.

Santolina chamaecyparissus

SANTOLINA

Also known as cotton lavender, santolina is a member of the daisy family, has an aromatic scent, and is useful as an insect repellent.

> **Soil** *Poor, well-drained.*
> **Parts used** *Flowering stems, and leaves.*
> **Medicinal** *Poor digestion, worms, stings, skin inflammation.*
> **Precaution** *Do not take internally.*

GROWING GUIDELINES

Sow seed in spring or take cuttings in late summer. Clip plant in spring. Pinch off fading flowers; don't overwater.
Growth habit Evergreen shrub; height to 2 feet (60 cm).
Flowers Summer; yellow, button-like blossoms.

HARVESTING AND STORING

Clip and bunch top 8–10 inches (20–25 cm) of foliage in summer; hang to dry. Collect flowers with stem at full bloom; hang to dry.

Santolina flowers rise above foliage on 4–6 inch (10–15 cm) stalks, and produce brownish seedpods.

Saponaria officinalis

SOAPWORT

This hardy herb is a localized roadside weed, sometimes also found on railway banks and waste land. As its name implies, soapwort lathers and cleans like soap.

Soil *Average, well-drained.*
Parts used *Leaves, leafy stems, flowers, rhizomes.*
Medicinal *Skin problems.*
Precaution *Not for internal use. Excess destroys red blood cells.*

GROWING GUIDELINES

Divide established plants or sow seed in fall or spring; water regularly. Drought tolerant once mature.

Growth habit Perennial; height to 3 feet (90 cm).

Flowers Midsummer to fall; pink to white blossoms.

HARVESTING AND STORING

Pick flowers, leaves, stems, and roots in fall, or as required. Clean, chop, and boil roots to make soapy solution.

Soapwort flowers have a sweet, fruity fragrance that perfumes the early evening air.

Fresh soapwort leaves soothe insect bites; boiled leaves form a lather that cleans delicate fabrics.

Sassafras albidum

SASSAFRAS

A tall, native American tree, sassafras produces an oil once used as a flavoring for cold and hot beverages. It has yellow, orange, and red foliage in the fall.

Soil Well-drained.
Parts used Leaves, roots, oil.
Medicinal Fevers, colic, arthritis, rashes, insect bites.
Precaution Excess can cause nausea. Oil may be carcinogenic.

GROWING GUIDELINES

Propagate by seed, suckers, or root cuttings. Young foliage smells of citrus; the roots and bark have a spicy scent.
Growth habit Deciduous; height 20–60 feet (6–18 m).
Flowers Spring; clusters of greenish-yellow blossoms.

HARVESTING AND STORING

Pick leaves in spring; lift roots in fall. Collect bark to produce oil, or dry. Store in airtight containers.

Sassafras thrives in just about any conditions, and provides a wonderful, fresh scent.

*Magnificent fall color defines sassafras
leaves, which are dried and powdered
to thicken soups.*

Plant winter savory with beans and cabbage to deter pests, and near onions to improve growth and flavor.

Satureja montana
WINTER SAVORY

This aromatic, peppery-flavored herb has been used in cooking for more than 2,000 years. It is also thought to be beneficial for digestion and skin problems.

> **Soil** *Poor, well-drained to dry.*
> **Parts used** *Leaves, shoots.*
> **Medicinal** *Indigestion, colic, nausea, diarrhea, insect bites.*
> **Culinary** *Leaves flavor sausages, salami, Provençal dishes.*

GROWING GUIDELINES

Sow seed shallowly in late spring. Take cuttings from established plants in summer, or divide older plants in spring or fall. Tip-prune to encourage bushiness.
Growth habit Perennial; 6–12 inches (15–30 cm).
Flowers Summer; white to pale purple blossoms.

HARVESTING AND STORING

Harvest fresh as required, or cut and dry foliage just before flowering.

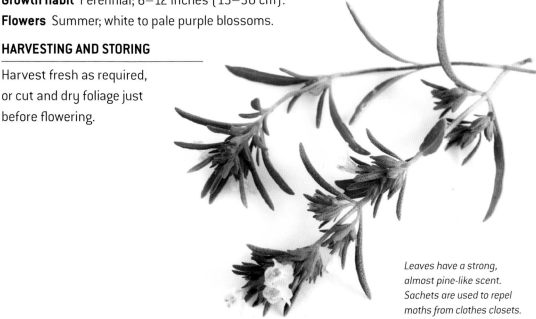

Leaves have a strong, almost pine-like scent. Sachets are used to repel moths from clothes closets.

Solidago spp.

GOLDENROD

Use the dried flowers of goldenrod for floral arrangements. Plant in masses or weave into ornamental plantings for spectacular, fall-flowering color.

Soil *Average to poor, well-drained.*
Parts used *Flowering tops, leaves.*
Medicinal *Internally for urinary infections, kidney stones, flatulence. Externally for wounds, insect bites, ulcers, sore throats.*

GROWING GUIDELINES

Easily grown from seed in early spring. Divide mature plants in spring or fall.
Growth habit Perennial; height 3–7 feet (90–210 cm).
Flowers Late summer to fall; yellow blooms from second year.

HARVESTING AND STORING

Collect leaves and tops during flowering; dry in bunches or on trays. Store in airtight conatiners.

Dried goldenrod flowers are used in medicinal preparations, and also to make a yellow dye.

Pollen-rich, flowering plumes attract butterflies and other beneficial insects to the garden.

Symphytum officinale

COMFREY

Grown more for its medicinal and ornamental value than for its culinary uses, comfrey was once thought to help repair broken bones.

Soil Rich, moist.
Parts used Leaves, roots.
Medicinal Bronchitis, arthritis, fractures, sprains.
Precaution Do not take internally; is a suspected carcinogen.

GROWING GUIDELINES

Propagate by seed, division, or root cuttings. Requires little care. Remove dead leaves in fall; divide every few years.
Growth habit Perennial; height 2–4 feet (60–120 cm).
Flowers Spring to summer; purple, pink, white, or cream blossoms.

HARVESTING AND STORING

Use leaves fresh or dried; leaves for drying are best picked in spring. Dig roots when plant has died down in fall; dry.

Use comfrey leaves in a salve or compress to treat bruises, wounds, ulcers, and sores.

Plant comfrey in full sun to maximize plant growth, and flower size and production.

Tagetes patula

FRENCH MARIGOLD

The genus is named after the Etruscan god, Tages, who practiced the art of water divination. Marigolds add color to any sunny garden.

Soil Well-drained, average.
Parts used Whole plant.
Medicinal Stomach upsets, eye inflammation, indigestion.
Culinary Leaves in salads, leaves and oil as food flavoring.

GROWING GUIDELINES

Propagate by seed sown in spring; readily self-sows. Pinch off flowering heads regularly.
Growth habit Annual; height to 1 foot (30 cm).
Flowers Summer to fall; yellow to orange-red blossoms.

HARVESTING AND STORING

Collect whole plant when flowering; dry. Pick leaves and flowers in summer; use fresh or dried. Extract oil from leaves.

French marigolds are an excellent companion plant for tomatoes; they repel slugs and other hungry pests.

Flowers are used to color dairy products. Fresh leaves, when rubbed, have a garlic-like odor.

Young, tender tamarind pods are pulled from the tree on forming and used as a seasoning.

Tamarindus indica
TAMARIND

This graceful tree has been cultivated in India for centuries. The name comes from the Arabic word for "date of India" and refers to the datelike pulp inside the pods.

Soil Light, well-drained.
Parts used Fruit.
Medicinal Fevers, asthma, ulcers, dysentery, poor digestion.
Culinary Fruit in lemonade-like drink; pulp in curries, sweets.

GROWING GUIDELINES

Propagate by seed sown when the temperature reaches 70°F (21°C), or by grafting.
Growth habit Evergreen; height to 80 feet (24 m).
Flowers Summer; pale yellow, fragrant blossoms.

HARVESTING AND STORING

Pick fruits when ripe; use fresh or dried.

Tamarind fruit contains kidney-shaped seeds encased in a sticky, brown pulp.

The dense, flat flowers of tansy attract butterflies and other beneficial insects to the garden.

Tanacetum vulgare
TANSY

This easy-to-grow herb has brilliant green foliage and yellow button-like flowers. It is an excellent companion for roses and a great pest repellent.

Dried tansy is placed in sachets and used around the house to control ants, mice, and flies.

GROWING GUIDELINES

Sow seed indoors in late winter; transplant outdoors after frosts have passed. Divide mature plants in spring or fall.
Growth habit Perennial; 3–4 feet (90–120 cm).
Flowers Late summer to fall; yellow blossoms.

HARVESTING AND STORING

Collect foliage during summer and dry.
Flowers dry well but lose their color.

Tansy flowers and leaves are used to make a green-gold dye.

Soil Well-drained, alkaline.
Parts used Leaves, flowers.
Culinary Leaves added to custard and cakes.
Precaution Oil is extremely toxic for internal and external use.

Taraxacum officinale

DANDELION

Some gardeners have learned to appreciate this lawn weed. If your thumb isn't green, try planting dandelions to boost your self-confidence!

Soil *Moderately fertile, moist.*
Parts used *Whole plant.*
Medicinal *Jaundice, urinary tract infections, constipation.*
Culinary *Leaves in salads, soups. Flowers for wine.*

GROWING GUIDELINES

Collect seed from a large-leaved specimen and sow shallowly in early spring.
Growth habit Perennial; height 6–12 inches (15–30 cm).
Flowers Spring to fall; golden flowers mature to feathery seed heads.

HARVESTING AND STORING

Pick leaves year round; blanch to decrease bitterness. Lift roots in fall, and slice into small pieces. Air-dry or roast in slow oven.

Dandelion flowers mature to puffballs of seeds that are dispersed by the wind.

Dandelion root tea targets the digestive and eliminative systems of the body, such as the kidneys.

Hardy thyme is ideal for rock gardens, and its multitude of nectar-rich flowers attract beneficial insects.

Thymus vulgaris
COMMON THYME

Easy-growing thyme is a favorite of cooks and gardeners. Delicately pretty in leaf and flower, a carpet of thyme makes a beautiful underplanting for roses.

Dried thyme is used in potpourris and moth-repelling sachets. It is less pungent than fresh foliage.

GROWING GUIDELINES

Sow seed shallowly indoors in late winter; tranplant outdoors in spring. Divide older plants in spring or take cuttings in late summer or fall.

Growth habit Shrub; height 6–15 inches (15–38 cm).

Flowers Midsummer; lilac to pink blossoms.

HARVESTING AND STORING

Snip foliage as required in summer, or harvest entirely twice per season; leave 3 inches (7.5 cm) of growth. Dry, or freeze in airtight bags.

Soil Well-drained.
Parts used Whole plant, oil.
Medicinal Bronchitis, indigestion, diarrhea, tonsilitis, arthritis, fungal infection, depression.
Culinary In bouquet garni; used to flavor stock, stuffings, sauces.
Precaution Not for pregnant women. May cause skin irritation.

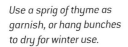

Use a sprig of thyme as garnish, or hang bunches to dry for winter use.

285

Trifolium pratense

RED CLOVER

A member of the legume family, red clover fixes nitrogen, an important element for all plant growth, in the soil. The flowering tops are used in herbal preparations.

Use dried to make a tea that is said to purify the blood, relieve coughs, and be a mild sedative.

GROWING GUIDELINES

Broadcast seed shallowly outdoors in early spring. Self-seeds freely; can be invasive.

Growth habit Perennial; 1–2 feet (30–60 cm).

Flowers From late spring; fragrant, tubular, bright pink-purple to red blooms.

HARVESTING AND STORING

Collect flowers at full bloom and dry on paper in shade. Store in airtight containers.

Soil *Light, moist, well-drained.*
Parts used *Flowering heads.*
Medicinal *Eczema, psoriasis, gout, degenerative diseases.*
Tip *Red clover can be grown as a permanent ground cover.*

Flowers attract beneficial insects, such as butterflies, and are used in herbal infusions and ointments .

Grow red clover as a living mulch; the nitrogen-fixing bacteria on the roots work to enhance soil fertility.

Trigonella foenum-graecum
FENUGREEK

A member of the same family as beans and clover, fenugreek is one of the world's oldest cultivated medicinal plants. The seeds make a laxative tea.

Dried and chopped leaves have a maple-like flavor, and are added to baked goods and confections.

GROWING GUIDELINES

Sow seed thickly outdoors in spring or indoors in pots.
Growth habit Annual; height 1–2 feet (30–60 cm).
Flowers Summer; white blossoms with pink or purple markings. Resembles garden pea flowers.

HARVESTING AND STORING

Collect pods when ripe but before they fall.
Dry seeds in sun.

Soil Rich, well-drained.
Parts used Leaves, seeds.
Medicinal Diabetes, cellulitis, gastric and bronchial complaints.
Culinary Middle Eastern, Indian, and African cooking.
Precaution Not suitable for pregnant women.

Seeds are roasted for use in curry powder, and also sprouted as a salad vegetable.

As a leguminous plant, fenugreek needs little nitrogen fertilizer, and actually enriches soil.

Climbing nasturtiums reach a height of 10 feet (3 m), and the flowers attract hummingbirds.

Tropaeolum majus
NASTURTIUM

A favorite of both gardeners and cooks, nasturtiums are a reliable source of flowering color throughout summer, and can be added to salads.

Soil Moist, well-drained.
Parts used Whole plant.
Medicinal Scurvy, baldness.
Culinary Chopped leaves add peppery flavor to eggs, cheese.

GROWING GUIDELINES

Sow seed outdoors when soil is warm in spring.
For best display, hold back on the nitrogen.
Growth habit Annual; height from 2 feet (60 cm).
Flowers From early summer; sweet-smelling, red, orange, or yellow, blossoms.

HARVESTING AND STORING

Snip young, fresh leaves and flowers as required in summer. In fall, pickle unopened buds for homemade capers.

Add fresh flowers, leaves, and buds to food, or use blossoms to make vinegar.

Urtica dioica
STINGING NETTLE

A noxious weed to gardeners, nettle is high in vitamins A and C, and is used by practitioners of homeopathic medicine.

Nettle tea is a recommended herbal treatment for anemia, arthritis, digestion, eczema, and migraines.

GROWING GUIDELINES

Self-sows readily and quickly multiplies from fleshy, creeping roots if left unchecked.
Growth habit Perennial; height 2–6 feet (60–180 cm).
Flowers Summer; tiny, greenish blossoms.

Soil *Moist, nitrogen-rich.*
Parts used *Whole plant.*
Medicinal *Externally for gout, sciatica, scalp and hair problems.*
Culinary *Young leaves as vegetable, in soups, nettle beer.*

HARVESTING AND STORING

Harvest whole plant above the root, just before flowering; hang in bunches to dry. Collect seeds and dry on paper.

Greenish male and female flowers occur on the same plant; the latter, pictured, are more densely clustered.

Be sure to wear heavy gloves when harvesting; leaves inject a substance that irritates the skin.

Valeriana officinalis

VALERIAN

This plant has powerful medicinal properties and has been prized for centuries as a tranquilizer. Drugs based upon it are still used today.

Soil Fertile, moist.
Parts used Rhizomes, roots, oil.
Medicinal Insomnia, migraine, anxiety, indigestion, ulcers.
Precaution Not suitable for people with liver problems.

GROWING GUIDELINES

Sow seed shallowly outdoors in spring, or propagate by division in spring or fall.
Growth habit Perennial; 3–5 feet (90–150 cm).
Flowers Summer; pale pink, white, or lavender blooms.

HARVESTING AND STORING

Lift roots in fall or spring, before new shoots form. Wash and dry until brittle. Stores well.

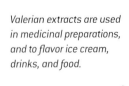

Valerian extracts are used in medicinal preparations, and to flavor ice cream, drinks, and food.

Leaves give off a sharp scent that attracts rats. Use bunches to attract and catch them.

Flowering valerian adds summer color and fragrance to a garden. The tubular blossoms have a sweet cherry scent.

Apply an organic mulch in spring to encourage flowering. The small, tubular blossoms have no scent.

Verbena officinalis

VERVAIN

This ancient herb has a long religious and medicinal history and was sacred to many cultures. It is still used to treat tiredness, stress, and minor abrasions.

> **Soil** Moist, well-drained.
> **Parts used** Whole plant.
> **Medicinal** Depression, asthma, migraine, jaundice, gum disease.
> **Precaution** Not for use during pregnancy.

GROWING GUIDELINES

Sow seed outdoors in spring, or take stem cuttings in summer. Self-seeds in light soil.
Growth habit Perennial; 1–2 feet (30–60 cm).
Flowers Summer to fall; pale lilac blossoms.

HARVESTING AND STORING

Pick foliage as required. Harvest the whole plant when it begins to flower; hang to dry.

Native to Western Asia, Europe, and the Himalayas, vervain may cause vomiting if used to excess.

Infuse dried vervain to make a tea that is used as a gargle for sore throats; use cold as an eyewash.

Wasabia japonica
WASABI

This native of Japan is generally found growing beside mountain streams. Wasabi is a condiment traditionally used to garnish raw fish and noodle dishes.

Soil *Rich, moist to wet.*
Parts used *Roots, leaves, stalks.*
Medicinal *For fish poisoning.*
Culinary *Powdered root flavors meat, fish dishes; leaves as vegetable, also pickled.*

GROWING GUIDELINES

Propagate in spring by seed kept moist, or by division of rootstock in spring and fall. Keep out of direct sun.
Growth habit Perennial; 8–16 inches (20–40 cm).
Flowers Spring; small, white blossoms.

HARVESTING AND STORING

Lift roots in spring or fall; use dried, fresh, ground, or preserved. Roots are mature 15–24 months after planting.

Wasabi covered peas are a spicy snack. Good-quality wasabi is sweet, and has a gentle scent.

Fresh wasabi root is used in Japanese cuisine as a seasoning, and an accompaniment to raw fish.

Zingiber officinale

GINGER

Fresh ginger has a zing that the powdered herb lacks. It has the double advantage of being both spicy and kind to your digestive system.

GROWING GUIDELINES

Plant rhizomes in pots in a compost containing coir, sand, and loam. Move pots outdoors in warm summers.
Growth habit Perennial; height 2–5 feet (60–150 cm).
Flowers Rarely blooms in containers; yellow-green-purple flowers.

HARVESTING AND STORING

Lift plant after one year and cut away as much root as needed; replant the remainder. Store fresh in the refrigerator, or dry shaved root and store in an airtight container.

For healthy growth, water ginger well during hot summer months and move indoors in winter.

Soil Fertile, moist, well-drained.
Parts used Rhizomes, oil.
Medicinal Motion and morning sickness, menstrual cramps, colds, coughs, muscle pain.
Culinary In curries, pickles, cakes.

Ginger tea is used to settle nausea. Add cinnamon, honey, and lemon to taste.

Fresh ginger root stores for up to a
month in the fridge; wrap in paper
towel and pop inside a plastic bag.

Stinging nettle

PLANT BY PLANT GUIDE

This quick gardening guide will help you decide what herb to plant based on growth habit and size, preferred soil type, and primary uses—culinary, medicinal, or other.

HERB	GROWTH FORM AND SIZE
Achillea millefolium Yarrow	Perennial, height to 3 feet (90 cm)
Agastache foeniculum Anise hyssop	Perennial, height to 3 feet (90 cm)
Agrimonia eupatoria Agrimony	Perennial, height 2–3 feet (60–90 cm)
Allium sativum Garlic	Perennial bulb, height to 2 feet (60 cm)
Allium schoenoprasum Chives	Perennial, height 6–12 inches (15–30 cm)
Aloe vera syn. A. barbadensis Aloe	Clump-forming perennial, to 1 foot (30 cm)
Aloysia triphylla Lemon verbena	Perennial woody shrub, to 10 feet (3 m)
Alpina galanga Galangal	Perennial, height to 6 feet (1.8 m)
Althaea officinalis Marsh mallow	Perennial, height to 4 feet (1.2 m)
Anethum graveolens Dill	Annual, height 2–3 feet (60–90 cm)
Angelica archangelica Angelica	Perennial, height 5–8 feet (1.5–2.4 m)
Anthriscus cerefolium Chervil	Annual, height 1–2 feet (30–60 cm)
Apium graveolens Wild celery	Perennial with bulbous roots, 3 feet (90 cm)
Arctium lappa Burdock	Biennial, height to 5 feet (1.5 m)
Armoracia rusticana Horseradish	Perennial, height 1–4 feet (30–120 cm)

Red clover

Peppermint

PREFERRED SOIL	PRIMARY USES (PARTS USED)
Fertile, well-drained soil	Medicinal, other (whole plant, dried flowers)
Rich, well-drained soil	Culinary, medicinal (leaves, flowers)
Light, well-drained soil	Medicinal (whole plant)
Rich, well-drained soil	Culinary, medicinal (bulbs)
Rich, well-drained soil	Culinary (fresh or dried leaves)
Gritty, well-drained soil	Medicinal (leaves, sap)
Fertile, light, well-drained soil	Culinary, medicinal, other (fresh or dried leaves)
Rich, moist, well-drained soil	Culinary, medicinal (rhizomes, oil)
Light, moist soil, neutral pH	Culinary, medicinal (leaves, roots)
Rich, well-drained soil	Culinary, medicinal (leaves, seeds, oil)
Cool, rich, moist soil	Culinary, medicinal (leaves, stems, seeds, roots)
Moist, rich, well-drained soil	Culinary, medicinal (leaves)
Rich, moist soil	Culinary, medicinal (whole plant, roots, seeds)
Deep, loose, moist, fertile soil	Culinary, medicinal (stems, roots, seeds)
Fertile, moist, well-drained soil	Culinary, medicinal (leaves, roots)

HERB	GROWTH FORM AND SIZE
Arnica montana Arnica	*Perennial, height to 2 feet (60 cm)*
Artemisia dracunculus French tarragon	*Perennial, height 2–4 feet (60–120 cm)*
Artemisia vulgaris Mugwort	*Perennial, height 3–6 feet (90–180 cm)*
Berberis vulgaris Barberry	*Deciduous shrub, height to 8 feet (2.4 m)*
Borago officinalis Borage	*Annual, height to 2 feet (60 cm)*
Brassica spp. Mustard	*Annual or biennial, 4–6 feet (1.2–1.8 m)*
Calendula officinalis Calendula	*Annual, height 1–2 feet (30–60 cm)*
Capparis spinosa Caper	*Prostrate shrub, height 3–6 feet (90–180 cm)*
Capsicum annuum Pepper	*Tender perennial, height 1–2 feet (30–60 cm)*
Carthamus tinctorius Safflower	*Annual, height 2–3 feet (60–90 cm)*
Carum carvi Caraway	*Biennial, height 1–2 feet (30–60 cm)*
Centaurea cyanus Cornflower	*Bushy annual, height to 3 feet (90 cm)*
Chamaemelum nobile Chamomile	*Low-growing perennial, height 6–9 inches (15–23 cm)*
Chrysanthemum coronarium Chrysanthemum	*Large perennial, 1–7 feet (30–210 cm)*
Chrysanthemum parthenium Feverfew	*Aromatic perennial, 8–24 inches (20–60 cm)*
Cichorium intybus Chicory	*Perennial, height 1–5 feet (30–150 cm)*
Coriandrum sativum Cilantro (coriander)	*Annual, height 1–3 feet (30–90 cm)*
Crocus sativus Saffron	*Perennial, height to 6 inches (15 cm)*
Cuminum cyminum Cumin	*Tender annual, height 10 inches (25 cm)*
Curcuma longa Turmeric	*Tall perennial, height 3 feet (90 cm)*

Winter savory

PREFERRED SOIL	PRIMARY USES (PARTS USED)
Dry, sandy, rich in humus	Medicinal (flowers)
Well-drained soil	Culinary, medicinal (leaves, oil)
Light, well-drained soil	Culinary, medicinal, other (leaves)
Moist, fertile, well-drained soil	Medicinal (leaves, bark, root, fruits)
Rich, moist, well-drained soil	Culinary, medicinal (leaves, flowers, seeds, oil)
Rich, well-drained soil	Culinary, medicinal (leaves, seeds, flowers, oil)
Average, well-drained soil	Culinary, medicinal (flower petals)
Well-drained, sandy soil	Culinary, medicinal (root bark, flower buds)
Light, evenly moist, well-drained	Culinary, medicinal (fruits)
Well-drained soil	Culinary, medicinal (flowers, seeds, oil)
Light, fertile garden soil	Culinary, medicinal (leaves, roots, seeds, oil)
Well-drained soil	Culinary, medicinal, other (flowers)
Moist, well-drained soil	Culinary, medicinal, other (flowers, oil)
Rich, well-drained soil	Culinary, medicinal (flowers)
Well-drained garden soil	Medicinal, other (whole plant, flowers, leaves)
Neutral to alkaline, well-drained	Culinary, medicinal (leaves, roots)
Fertile, well-drained soil	Culinary, other (leaves, seeds, roots, oil)
Light, fertile, well-drained soil	Culinary, medicinal, other (flower stigmas)
Light, well-drained soil	Culinary, medicinal, other (seeds)
Rich, well-drained soil	Culinary, medicinal, other (rhizomes)

HERB	GROWTH FORM AND SIZE
Cymbopogon citratus Lemongrass	*Tender perennial, height 6 feet (1.8 m)*
Echinacea purpurea Echinacea	*Tall perennial, height 4 feet (1.2 m)*
Elettaria cardamomum Cardamom	*Tender perennial, 6–10 feet (1.8–3 m)*
Equisetum spp. Horsetail	*Perennial, 4–18 inches (10–45 cm)*
Filipendula ulmaria Meadowsweet	*Hardy, woody perennial, height 4 feet (1.2 m)*
Foeniculum vulgare Fennel	*Semi-hardy perennial, height 4 feet (1.2 m)*
Ginkgo biloba Ginkgo	*Deciduous tree, 80–120 feet (24–36 m)*
Glycyrrhiza glabra Licorice	*Hardy perennial, height to 5 feet (1.5 m)*
Hamamelis virginiana Witch hazel	*Deciduous shrub, 8–15 feet (2.4–4.5 m)*
Helianthus annuus Sunflower	*Giant annual, 3–10 feet (90–300 cm)*
Hypericum perforatum St John's wort	*Weedy perennial, 10–36 inches (25–90 cm)*
Hyssopus officinalis Hyssop	*Semi-evergreen perennial, to 2 feet (60 cm)*
Iris 'Florentina' Orris	*Perennial, height to 2 ½ feet (75 cm)*
Juniperus communis Common juniper	*Upright or prostrate shrub, to 20 feet (6 m)*
Laurus nobilis Sweet bay	*Evergreen tree, 10–49 feet (3–15 m)*
Lavandula angustifolia English Lavender	*Shrubby perennial, 2–3 feet (60–90 cm)*
Levisticum officinale Lovage	*Perennial, height to 6 feet (1.8 m)*
Melissa officinalis Lemon balm	*Perennial, height 1–2 feet (30–60 cm)*
Mentha spp. Mint	*Perennial, height to 2 ½ feet (75 cm)*
Mentha x. piperita Peppermint	*Perennial: height to 4 feet (120 cm)*

Chervil

PREFERRED SOIL

PRIMARY USES (PARTS USED)

PREFERRED SOIL	PRIMARY USES (PARTS USED)
Rich, well-drained soil	Culinary, medicinal, other (leaves, stems, oil)
Humus-rich, well-drained soil	Medicinal (roots, rhizomes)
Moist, humus-rich soil	Culinary, medicinal, other (seeds, oil)
Humus-rich, moist soil	Medicinal (stems)
Rich, wet soil	Medicinal, other (whole plant, flowers)
Humus-rich, well-drained soil	Culinary, medicinal (leaves, stems, roots, seeds, oil)
Deep, moist, humus-rich soil	Culinary, medicinal (leaves, seeds)
Deep, moist, humus-rich soil	Culinary, medicinal, other (roots, stolons)
Moist, humus-rich soil	Medicinal, other (leaves, branches, twigs, bark)
Rich, well-drained soil	Culinary, medicinal, other (whole plant, seeds, oil)
Well-drained to dry soil	Medicinal, other (whole plant)
Light, well-drained soil	Culinary, medicinal, other (whole plant, leaves)
Deep, rich, well-drained soil	Medicinal, other (rhizomes)
Adaptable to most soil conditions	Culinary, medicinal, other (berries, oil)
Rich, well-drained soil	Culinary, medicinal (leaves)
Light, well-drained, limey soil	Culinary, medicinal, other (flowers, oil)
Fertile, moist, well-drained soil	Culinary, medicinal (leaves, stems, roots, seeds, oil)
Any well-drained soil	Culinary, medicinal (whole plants, leaves, oil)
Rich, moist, well-drained soil	Culinary, medicinal, other (whole plant, leaves, oil)
Rich, moist, well-drained soil	Culinary, medicinal, other (whole plant, leaves, oil)

HERB	GROWTH FORM AND SIZE
Monarda didyma Bee balm (bergamot)	*Perennial, height 3–4 feet (90–120 cm)*
Myrrhis odorata Sweet cicely	*Perennial, height to 3 feet (90 cm)*
Nasturtium officinale Watercress	*Aquatic perennial*
Nepeta cataria Catmint	*Perennial, height 1–3 feet (30–90 cm)*
Ocimum basilicum Sweet basil	*Annual, height to 2 feet (60 cm)*
Ocimum basilicum 'Horapha' Thai basil	*Annual, height to 18 inches (45 cm)*
Oenothera biennis Evening primrose	*Tall biennial, height 5 feet (1.5 m)*
Origanum majorana Sweet marjoram	*Tender perennial, height to 2 feet (60 cm)*
Origanum vulgare Oregano	*Bushy perennial, 1–2½ feet (30–75 cm)*
Panax ginseng Ginseng	*Perennial, height to 3 feet (90 cm)*
Passiflora incarnata Passionflower	*Climbing vine, 25–30 feet (7.5–9 m)*
Petroselinum crispum Parsley	*Biennial, height 8–12 inches (20–30 cm)*
Petroselinum crispum 'Italian' Italian parsley	*Biennial, height to 1 foot (30 cm)*
Pimpinella anisum Anise	*Annual, height to 2 feet (60 cm)*
Piper nigrum Pepper	*Climbing perennial, height 12 feet (4 m)*
Plantago major Plantain	*Perennial, 6–18 inches (15–45 cm)*
Rosa spp. Dog rose	*Perennial, height to 10 feet (3 m)*
Rosmarinus officinalis Rosemary	*Evergreen shrub, 2–6 feet (60–180 cm)*
Rubus idaeus Raspberry	*Deciduous shrub with suckering canes*
Rumex acetosa Sorrel	*Hardy perennial, height 2 feet (60 cm)*

Barberry

PREFERRED SOIL

PRIMARY USES (PARTS USED)

PREFERRED SOIL	PRIMARY USES (PARTS USED)
Rich, moist, light garden soil	Culinary, medicinal, other (leaves, flowers)
Moist, humus-rich, well-drained soil	Culinary, medicinal (leaves, roots, seeds)
Alkaline, flowing water	Culinary, medicinal (leaves)
Dry, sandy garden soil	Culinary, medicinal, other (whole plant, leaves)
Rich, moist soil	Culinary, medicinal, other (leaves, stems, seeds, oil)
Rich, well-drained	Culinary, medicinal, other (leaves. stems, seeds, oil)
Dry, sandy soil	Culinary, medicinal, other (oil from seeds, roots)
Light, well-drained soil	Culinary, medicinal, other (leaves, seeds, oil)
Average, well-drained, garden soil	Culinary, medicinal, other (whole plant, leaves, oil)
Moist, well-drained soil	Medicinal (roots, flowers)
Fertile, well-drained soil	Culinary, medicinal (whole plant, fruits)
Moderately rich, well-drained soil	Culinary, medicinal, other (leaves, roots, seeds, oil)
Consistently moist	Culinary, medicinal (leaves)
Poor, light, well-drained soil	Culinary, medicinal (leaves, seeds, oil)
Rich, moist soil	Culinary, medicinal (fruits)
Moist, well-drained soil	Culinary, medicinal (leaves, roots)
Well-drained, moist soil	Culinary, medicinal, other (petals, fruits)
Light, well-drained soil	Culinary, medicinal, other (leaves, oil, flowering tops)
Rich, well-drained soil	Culinary, medicinal (leaves, fruits)
Fertile, moist soil	Culinary, medicinal, other (leaves)

HERB	GROWTH FORM AND SIZE
Salvia officinalis Sage	*Perennial shrub, height 1–2 feet (30–60 cm)*
Salvia sclarea Clary	*Biennial or perennial, 2–5 feet (60–150 cm)*
Sambucus nigra Elder	*Deciduous shrub or tree, to 30 feet (9 m)*
Santolina chamaecyparissus Santolina	*Evergreen shrub, height to 2 feet (60 cm)*
Saponaria officinalis Soapwort	*Rhizomatous perennial, height 1–3 feet (30–90 cm)*
Sassafras albidum Sassafras	*Deciduous tree, height 20–60 feet (6–18 m)*
Satureja montana Winter savory	*Evergreen perennial, height 6–12 inches (15–30 cm)*
Solidago spp. Goldenrod	*Perennial, height 3–7 feet (90–210 cm)*
Symphytum officinale Comfrey	*Perennial, height 2–4 feet (60–120 cm)*
Tagetes patula French marigold	*Annual, height 1 foot (30 cm)*
Tamarindus indica Tamarind	*Evergreen tree, height 80 feet (24 m)*
Tanacetum vulgare Tansy	*Perennial, height 3–4 feet (90–120 cm)*
Taraxacum officinale Dandelion	*Perennial, height 6–12 inches (15–30 cm)*
Thymus vulgaris Common thyme	*Variable shrub, height 1–1½ feet (30–45 cm)*
Trifolium pratense Red clover	*Perennial, height 1–2 feet (30–60 cm)*
Trigonella foenum-graecum Fenugreek	*Annual, height 1–2 feet (30–60 cm)*
Tropaeolum majus Nasturtium	*Annual, height 1–2 feet (30–60 cm)*
Urtica dioica Stinging nettle	*Herbaceous perennial, 2–6 feet (60–180 cm)*
Valeriana officinalis Valerian	*Herbaceous perennial, 3–5 feet (90–150 cm)*
Verbena officinalis Vervain	*Perennial, height 1–2 feet (30–60 cm)*
Wasabia japonica Wasabi	*Hardy perennial, 8–16 inches (20–40 cm)*
Zingiber officinale Ginger	*Tropical perennial, height 2–5 feet (60–150 cm)*

Rosemary

PREFERRED SOIL	PRIMARY USES (PARTS USED)
Well-drained garden soil	*Culinary, medicinal, other (leaves, oil, flowers)*
Average, well-drained soil	*Culinary, medicinal, other (leaves, flowers, seeds, oil)*
Moist, rich, well-drained soil	*Culinary, medicinal, other (leaves, bark, flowers, fruits)*
Poor, well-drained soil	*Medicinal, other (leaves, flowering stems)*
Average, well-drained soil	*Medicinal, other (leaves, leafy stems, rhizomes)*
Well-drained garden soil	*Culinary, medicinal, other (leaves, roots, oil)*
Poor, well-drained soil	*Culinary, medicinal, other (leaves, shoots)*
Average to poor, well-drained soil	*Medicinal (leaves, flowering tops)*
Rich, moist garden soil	*Medicinal (leaves, roots)*
Well-drained, average soil	*Medicinal, culinary, other (whole plant)*
Light, well-drained soil	*Culinary, medicinal, other (fruits)*
Well-drained garden soil	*Culinary, other (leaves, flowers)*
Moderately fertile, moist soil	*Culinary, medicinal (whole plant, leaves, roots, flowers)*
Average, well-drained soil	*Culinary, medicinal, other (whole plant, leaves, flowers, oil)*
Light, moist, well-drained soil	*Medicinal (flowering tops)*
Moist, rich garden soil	*Culinary, medicinal (leaves, seeds)*
Average, moist, well-drained soil	*Culinary, medicinal (whole plant, leaves, flowers)*
Most soils	*Culinary, medicinal, other (whole plants, leaves)*
Fertile, moist, garden soil	*Medicinal, other (rhizomes, roots, oil)*
Ordinary, moist, well-drained soil	*Medicinal (whole plant)*
Rich, moist to wet soil	*Culinary, medicinal (roots, leaves, leaf stalks)*
Moist, fertile, well-drained soil	*Culinary, medicinal (rhizomes, oil)*

GLOSSARY

annual A plant that has a life span of one year or less.

biennial A plant that has a life span of two years.

bouquet garni A bunch of herbs, most commonly including a bay leaf, thyme, and parsley or chervil tied together with string, or in a muslin bag. It is used in the cooking of soups, stews, and sauces and removed before serving. The essential oils of the herbs provide a subtle flavor and aroma.

compress A pad of soft material moistened with a warm herbal infusion or decoction and placed on a wound for medicinal purposes.

cutting A section taken from the stem of a plant in order to reproduce the plant.

decoction An extract of a herb made by simmering the roots and bark of a plant (most commonly dried) in water.

division The propagation of a plant by removing a section from the root and replanting.

fixative A substance that is added to the base of potpourri to preserve the fragrance. Fixatives can be of animal origin, such as ambergris, civet, and musk, or derived from plants, such as orris root, vetiver root, rose attar, dried rosemary, sweet flag, or tonka beans. One tablespoon of fixative is used for each quart (liter) of dried base.

infusion The extract of an herb made by steeping or soaking the flowers, leaves, and stems of the plant in boiling water.

layering The propagation of a plant by means of burying one of its still-attached, long, flexible stems into the soil next to the plant.

marinade A liquid in which foods are soaked in order to tenderize and flavor them.

Commonly meat or poultry is soaked in a marinade containing wine, vinegar, and herbs for several hours or overnight.

mulch A material that is used to cover the surface of your garden soil in order to keep the soil warmer in winter and cooler in summer, to retain moisture, and to hinder the growth of weeds. Mulch can be an organic material, such as compost, grass clippings, or shredded leaves, or an inorganic material, such as black plastic.

over-wintering Growing plants indoors during winter.

perennial A plant that has a life span of more than two years.

potpourri Long-lasting, fragrant mixtures of dried herbs and other crushed plant material.

poultice A paste made of minced, dried, or fresh herbs, oatmeal, and hot water. A poultice is used directly on the skin to draw out infection and relieve muscle aches.

propagate To reproduce a plant.

rhizome The underground runner or stem of a plant.

taproot The strong, tapering central root of a plant that grows straight down in search of water and nutrients.

tincture An extract of an herb made by soaking the dried plant in alcohol for six weeks. Tinctures are much more concentrated and their potency lasts longer than decoctions or infusions.

tussie-mussies Miniature herbal bouquets used to communicate sentiment.

INDEX

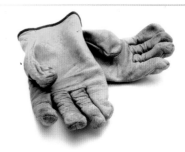

HERBS

ACKNOWLEDGMENTS

All maps and illustrations © Weldon Owen Pty Ltd. All photographs © istockphoto.com, except pages 61 and 296 sciencephoto.com, and page 298 shutterstock.com.